THE
MORECAMBE
& WISE
QUIZ BOOK

Paul Burton has a prolific number of writing, producing and directing credits to his name. Since 1989, Paul has both founded and run several of his own arts projects, including community film and television projects and more recently a hospital radio project. Paul is also a passionate British film, television and radio historian. Writing *The Morecambe & Wise Quiz Book* has been a labour of love for the life-long fan of the much-loved and missed performers. For more details about Paul Burton, please visit his official website: www.paulburton.org.uk

THE
MORECAMBE
& WISE
QUIZ BOOK

Paul Burton

Foreword by
Ray Galton OBE and Alan Simpson OBE

BOOKS

This book is dedicated to Ann Hamilton, who, in my opinion, was the third member of Morecambe & Wise, and to the memory of Eric Morecambe and Ernie Wise.

First published in Great Britain in 2008 by
JR Books, 10 Greenland Street, London NW1 0ND
www.jrbooks.com

A catalogue record for this book is available from the British Library.

ISBN 978-1-906217-74-7

1 3 5 7 9 10 8 6 4 2

Printed in Great Britain by Cromwell Press

Contents

Acknowledgements   vii
Foreword by Ray Galton OBE and Alan Simpson OBE   viii
Introduction   ix

Questions
Eric Morecambe   3
Ernie Wise   8
Pot Luck 1   12
Stage   16
Radio   23
Television   26
Eric and Ernie Live   49
The Sweeney   51
Supporting Cast   54
Special Guests   58
Complete The Names   68
Production Team   72
Pot Luck 2   83
Film   85
Records   99
Catchphrases   100

Books   101

Luton Town FC   103

Bring Me Sunshine Tribute Show   105

The Eric Morecambe Statue   107

The Play What I Wrote   108

Pot Luck 3   109

Answers   113

Eric Morecambe and Ernie Wise : A Chronology   157

Afterword by Paul Zenon   170

Websites   171

Bibliography   172

Acknowledgements

First of all I would like to take this opportunity to thank Ray Galton and Alan Simpson for taking the time and trouble to write the foreword for this book. My sincere thanks also go to the following people for contributing their personal thoughts, feelings and/or memories on Morecambe & Wise, which are interpolated with the questions in the book: Bobby Ball, David Benson, Phil Collinge and Andy Lord, Andrew Collins, Jimmy Cricket, Richard Digance, Wayne Dobson, Harry Fielder, Tony Hatch, Tammy Jones, Helen Lederer, Norman Lovett, Graham McCann, Vicki Michelle, Billy Pearce, Susie Peirce, Dave Prowse, Angela Rippon, Roger Wash and Paul Welsh. And last, but certainly not least, I would like to thank Paul Zenon for writing the afterword for this book. There are many other people I would like to thank here personally for their various forms of help during my research for this book, but in doing so the list would be endless! So to those people – and you know who you are – I would like to just say a huge thank you.

Foreword

Probably best known as the writers of the classic sitcoms *Hancock's Half Hour* and *Steptoe & Son*, Ray Galton OBE and Alan Simpson OBE (known collectively as Galton and Simpson) have also written extensively together for film, television and radio.

'During our long and varied career we had the pleasure of working with most of the top-line comedians in the business, some of whom actually survived the experience. The one notable exception was Morecambe & Wise, whom we never wrote for, something we always regretted, they being one of the few double acts who were worth twice as much money as the best solo acts. In actual fact, they were really a treble act. We must never forget their writer, the superb Eddie Braben. This book is a fitting tribute to their genius.'

Ray Galton OBE and Alan Simpson OBE

Introduction

My earliest memories of watching Morecambe & Wise are of the shows they made for Thames Television. Indeed, the earliest sketch that I can remember is from one such Thames show. The sequence saw Ernie opening a door, which was situated at the back of the stage, and a very attractive woman emerging. She seductively enticed Ernie to accompany her through the door with the obvious suggestion that she had more than merely talking about playwriting on her mind! Eric, thinking he'd get the same treatment, opened a nearby door to be faced with an old hag, who proceeded to beat him about the head with a rolling pin!

A simple end-of-show sketch, arguably not as memorable as many of the sketches or routines that came as part of Eric and Ernie's long television career, but certainly one that has stayed vividly with me. As has the short burst of introductory words that were set to the Thames Television ident. fanfare music which heralded the start of the shows broadcast by the company on the ITV network: 'Here they are now, Morecambe & Wise'.

I was still only 10 years old when Eric passed away and despite not being related to Eric, I, like a very high percentage of the population of this country – a country then still reeling from the loss of another comedy legend, Tommy Cooper – felt that I had lost someone very special to me. Someone who will never be replaced. One of the reasons being, as Michael Parkinson pointed out in the compilation show, *The Sunshine Boys*, the circumstances under which Eric and Ern became a double act are no longer there. Many of the music halls and variety theatres in which the duo learned their craft during their long and hard slog to the top have since gone on to become cinemas, bingo halls or, worse still, have long since been demolished. Fortunately, though, several of these buildings have survived and are still open as theatres. But the world of entertainment that Morecambe & Wise worked in when they first started has, sadly, changed or has simply just gone, and with it the opportunity for any potential new double acts or comedians to come along and take their place. Not that I believe anyone ever could. The expression 'they broke the mould' could have been invented for Morecambe & Wise. They were special, extra special, and cannot be replaced.

My love for both Eric and Ernie has always come in equal measure. And while it's true to say that both men would have had successful careers in show business if they hadn't met, there is no doubt that they were a comedy force to be reckoned with when they came together and worked as a double act. Both complemented each other's strengths perfectly and created an act that inspired warmth, devotion and, I would go as far as to say, love from the British public. So when Ernie passed away I felt the same loss as when Eric left us.

No one should ever underestimate just how hard Morecambe & Wise worked to achieve their deserved success. In these days when, it seems, everyone wants to be famous and achieve success, usually without any effort, such individuals should take note of how hard Eric Morecambe and Ernie Wise worked! They both gave everything and this included, arguably, their health as a result.

Despite the fact that Eric and Ernie are no longer with us, we are, thanks to the blessing of the various film, television and radio productions they made over the years, still able to continue to experience the magic they created. Consequently, Morecambe & Wise now have numerous fans who weren't even alive when their many memorable radio and television shows were being recorded.

I consider myself to be very lucky to have been on this planet when Eric and Ernie were still alive and working together, and to have been able to watch many of their television shows when they were being broadcast for the very first time, although I still feel sad that I never managed to see them live on stage or attend any of their television recordings. I was simply born slightly too late.

Even as a boy, I knew Morecambe & Wise were extra special. Watching comedy on television as a boy was as important to me as learning to read and write. Like some kind of comedy sponge, I soaked up and enjoyed as much comedy as I could as a child – and still do! And Eric Morecambe and Ernie Wise, then as now, have always been two of my real favourite comedy practitioners. They may have left us but I don't have to believe it if I don't want to! Seeing them at their peak on their classic television shows can make one believe that they are still very much alive.

I am proud to admit that I enjoy Morecambe & Wise's film work and I have always loved watching all of their Thames Television work, including *Night Train to Murder*, just as much as their BBC archive of television and radio work. So when the opportunity came to write this new quiz book, the first known quiz book on Morecambe & Wise to be printed, you can imagine how delighted I was. It was the chance to produce a piece of work dedicated to 'The Boys', as they were always known, that has never been published before. Don't get me wrong, there are many excellent books out there on Eric, Ernie, and Morecambe & Wise, especially those written by Eric's son, Gary Morecambe, but this is the first time a whole quiz book has been dedicated to the comedy duo. It's an opportunity to share my love of Morecambe & Wise and remind people of their various achievements, including those that have been criminally under-appreciated or simply forgotten.

While writing and researching this book I started to live a strange life, one that literally became dominated by Eric and Ernie. Most of my waking hours were spent watching or listening to their material. It put me in a privileged position: here was I, actually able to really study their television work, sketch by sketch, in order to find inspiration for the questions in this book. When not watching DVDs and videos of the legendary act, I found myself reading endless books written on Eric and/or Ernie. I became completely absorbed, even a little obsessed. I found myself rediscovering sketches and routines that I hadn't seen for years. With this, memories came flooding back of what I was doing or feeling when I had seen a sketch or programme for the first time years ago. But that made me realise that we, as a nation, not only remember Morecambe & Wise and their work, but also what we were doing or feeling at the time we first viewed a show. For instance, Eric and Ernie will be forever linked with the season of goodwill. For as we all know, some of Morecambe & Wise's finest moments and highest ratings were for their classic Christmas shows. This very fact has inspired one of Morecambe & Wise's writers, Eddie Braben, on numerous occasions to point out that, understandably, this put extra pressure on 'The Boys' – and himself, of course – to continue to keep up their high standard of performance and, in his case, of the writing of the show.

Morecambe & Wise are, as Eric's widow once said, 'icons in this country' and thus I took the responsibility of compiling this book very seriously. I hope reading and answering the various questions will bring back many happy memories of Eric and Ernie and their work.

So sit back and prepare to test your knowledge of Morecambe & Wise. From their stage appearances to their television work, this book features 1,000 questions that, I hope, will both educate and entertain Eric and Ernie fans both old and new. And if that wasn't enough, then you can also read thoughts shared by just a few of the many well-known people who worked with, knew or are simply just fans of Eric and Ern, together with a few 'Did You Know?' facts included along the way. There is also an Eric Morecambe and Ernie Wise Chronology included at the back of this book. But as this features several facts on 'The Boys', I advise that you don't read it until you have tested your knowledge with the questions. That would be cheating! Or maybe you would prefer to see it as swotting up on Morecambe & Wise first. It's up to you.

Writing this book has been a pleasure and a joy, and I hope that in the process of reading this new book you will be reminded of the many performances of sheer brilliance that Eric and Ernie brought to millions of people during their lifetime. They really did 'Bring Us Sunshine' – and may their legacy continue to entertain and inspire forever.

'Morecambe & Wise really did carve a permanent home for themselves in the lives of the British public. I think their "Staying Power" is a tribute to the quality of their comic genius and your book will no doubt be a further tribute to that genius.'

Angela Rippon, TV presenter

'Yes they brought sunshine, yes they brought laughter. In fact, they made you laugh out loud, not just smile or giggle, and they still do with their legacy today; but more than that, they brought families together to share in it. Quite an epitaph.'

Vicki Michelle, actress

Questions

Eric Morecambe

See how many of the 50 questions in this section, which all relate to the tall one with the glasses, Eric Morecambe, you can answer correctly.

1. What was Eric's real full name?
2. On which date was Eric born?
3. What was the name of the girl with whom Eric performed in a song and dance act when he was a boy?
4. Which ukele-playing Lancashire performer was a childhood hero of Eric's?
5. At what age did Eric leave school to start his career in show business – 12, 13 or 14?
6. What was the name of the double act that Eric used to impersonate in his solo act?
7. In 1939 Eric won a talent competition, but what was his prize?
8. True or false: Eric spent time as a Bevin Boy during the Second World War?
9. Name the entertainment organisation which Eric was briefly a member of during the Second World War?
10. True or false: the husband of singer Adelaide Hall, Bert Hicks, suggested that Eric change his second name to Morecambe?
11. At which theatre did Eric meet his future wife, Joan Bartlett?
12. On what date did Eric and Joan get married – 10 December 1952, 11 December 1952 or 12 December 1952?

13. At which seaside town did Eric's in-laws once run a hotel?

14. In which year did Eric pass his driving test?

15. What was Eric's first-ever car?

16. In which year did Eric and his wife, Joan, buy their first house?

17. Which of Eric's children was born first – Gail or Gary?

18. What was the name of one of Eric's children's dogs – Charlie, Chester or Chips?

19. True or false: Eric introduced Roy Castle to his future wife, Fiona?

20. In which year did Eric suffer his first heart attack?

21. What was the name of the man who helped to get Eric to a hospital in Leeds when he was suffering his first heart attack?

22. In which country did Eric first have a holiday villa?

23. What was the name of the ventriloquist's dummy that Eric used on stage?

24. In which year did Eric give his daughter, Gail, away at her wedding – 1974, 1975 or 1976?

25. What is the name of Eric's adopted son – Andy, Mark or Steven?

26. True or false: Eric was a strong swimmer?

27. What was the name of the fictitious *Treasure Island* character whom Eric enjoyed impersonating?

28. What was the name of Eric's long-time chauffeur – Mike Fountain, Mike Harper or Mike Walsh?

29. True or false: Eric was a self-confessed hypochondriac?

30. What was the registration of Eric's brown Rolls-Royce?

31. What was the name of the charity which Eric started with Elton John and Jimmy Hill?

Did You Know?

Eric Morecambe had an impressive collection of hand-carved meerschaum pipes of naked women, kings' heads, and even one shaped like a mermaid. But his real passion was for collecting pocket watches and, at the peak of his collecting, he is said to have owned about 50 of them.

32. Which university presented Eric with an honorary degree?

33. In which year did Eric undergo heart bypass surgery?

34. In which year was Eric's first novel, *Mr Lonely*, first published?

35. What was the title of the film in which Eric had the small role of Major Maxton-Weir?

36. What were the titles of the two novels that Eric wrote for children?

37. What was the name of the silent film for which Eric filmed his scenes in both 1982 and 1983?

38. What was the title of the fishing-related book that Eric wrote?

39. What was the title of the former ITV sports programme on which Eric once made a special appearance?

40. What was the title of the book that Eric collaborated on with his son, Gary?

41. True or false: during his later years Eric kept tropical fish?

42. On which date did Eric pass away?

43. Who was the entertainer who read the main address at Eric's funeral?

44. What was the title of Eric's second adult novel, which was completed after his death?

45. What was the title of the book written by Eric's wife after his death?

46. How much did one of Eric's pipes sell for on the website eBay in January 2008 – £145, £155 or £165?

47. Complete the title of the following television documentary: *The Heart ___ ___ ___ Eric Morecambe.*

Gail Morecambe

Gail Morecambe is a watercolour artist and daughter of Eric. She had a crush on the singer Gene Pitney and her father invited her to a show in which Pitney appeared. During a break in recording, in front of everyone, Eric announced: 'My daughter's in love with you.' Gail recalled in the book *Memories of Eric*:

'I think poor Mr Pitney said something like "Oh, that's nice." Then Dad said, "She's in the audience tonight, would you like to meet her? Stand up, Gail. Where are you?"

Many thoughts flashed through my mind at this point, some of them murderous, but I decided it would be better to stand up quickly, smile and sit down again. Rows of heads turned to see where I was. Mr Pitney kindly said, "Oh, she's lovely," to which my father replied, "Yes, we call her sparrow legs." I was very self-conscious about my skinny legs and now I wished I'd worn trousers and hoped I wouldn't even have to meet Gene Pitney after the show.'

48. In which year was the television documentary
    The Unforgettable Eric Morecambe first broadcast?

49. How much was Eric's brown Rolls-Royce sold for at auction in
    2006 – £23,467, £24,467 or £25,467?

50. What has Eric and Joan's first home together subsequently
    been turned into – a police station, a nursing home or a bed-
    and-breakfast?

Ernie Wise

Now see how many of the following 50 questions in this section, which all relate to the one with the short, fat, hairy legs, Ernie Wise, you can answer correctly.

51. What was Ernie Wise's real name?

52. In which northern city was Ernie born?

53. On what date was Ernie born – 27 October 1925, 27 November 1925 or 27 December 1925?

54. What were the names of Ernie's parents?

55. Ernie started his show business career as part of a double act with his father, but what was the main name of this act?

56. How much did Ernie receive for his first-ever radio broadcast?

57. In which year did the impresario Bryan Michie audition Ernie at the Leeds Empire?

58. True or false: Ernie appeared in a show at the Alhambra, Bradford, entitled *The Nignog Revue*?

59. What was the name of the well-known comedian who Ernie worked with in his famous *Band Wagon* show in 1939?

60. To earn himself some extra money when he was young, what job did Ernie take?

61. How many years did Ernie spend in the merchant navy – one, two or three?

62. Where did Ernie meet his future wife, Doreen Blythe?

63. On which romantic day of the year did Ernie propose to his wife?

64. On what date did Ernie and Doreen get married – 17 January 1953, 18 January 1953 or 19 January 1953?

65. In which Cambridgeshire town did Ernie and his wife Doreen once live?

66. How many children did Ernie and his wife, Doreen, have – none, one or two?

67. True or false: Ernie's wife once ran a dancing school?

68. What tragic news event did Ernie once recall had been reported while he and Eric were both on stage receiving their first-ever BAFTA award in 1963?

69. What size shoes did Ernie take?

70. Which of the following did Ernie accidentally do just prior to a pantomime performance in 1964 – he swallowed a front tooth, he tripped and fell or he sprained his wrist?

71. True or false: Ernie was chosen to draw the first-ever Premium Bond number in Britain?

72. What was the name of the BBC2 gardening programme Ernie chose in the 'My Choice' column in an edition of the *Radio Times* in September 1973?

73. True or false: Ernie once had a holiday home in Malta?

74. What was the name of the nostalgia-related show, once hosted by the writer and broadcaster Denis Norden, in which Ernie appeared alongside comedy partner Eric in 1978?

75. What was the name of the American television situation comedy in which Ernie made a special guest appearance: *Too Close to Call*, *Too Hard to Tell* or *Too Close for Comfort*?

76. On which date did Ernie make the first-ever mobile phone call in Britain – 1 January 1985, 1 January 1986 or 1 January 1987?

77. What was the name of the Thames Television panel game show in which Ernie appeared in the 1980s?

78. What was the name of the Ray Cooney West End farce which Ernie appeared in?

79. True or false: Ernie once helped front a campaign for *Keep Britain Tidy* which saw him literally being pushed into a rubbish bin?

80. Complete the title of the LWT chat show on which Ernie appeared in 1987: _____ *and Company*.

81. Ernie played the role of William Cartwright in which West End musical in 1987?

Did You Know?

Ernie Wise was once invited to become a presenter on *The Basil Brush Show*.

82. What was the name of the 1980s and 1990s television-themed quiz show hosted by Noel Edmonds which Ernie made an appearance on?

83. True or false: Ernie worked with the singer Lulu on the West End stage?

84. What was the name of the heart charity that Ernie helped to raise funds for in 1989?

85. Who did Ernie dedicate his autobiography to?

86. In which year was Ernie the subject of *This is Your Life* – 1990, 1991 or 1992?

87. What was the name of the last-ever television show broadcast from the BBC Television Theatre (prior to being sold by the corporation) on which Ernie briefly appeared – *Crackerjack*, *That's Life* or *Wogan*?

88. Who were the two other guests who appeared with Ernie on a series of *Morecambe & Wise* compilation videos in the early 1990s?

89. What was the title of the last-ever pantomime Ernie appeared in?

90. How many telethons did Ernie appear on in New Zealand – two, three or four?

91. What was the name of the Channel 4 daytime quiz show on which Ernie often appeared as a guest?

92. What was the name of the daytime entertainment show Ernie appeared on in November 1991?

93. Ernie had a home on the banks of which river?

94. Whereabouts in America did Ernie have a winter home?

95. What was the title of Ernie's autobiography?

96. What was the title of the BBC television documentary that featured Ernie as its subject in 1993?

97. In which year did Ernie announce his retirement from show business?

98. On which date did Ernie pass away?

99. Which television executive read the eulogy at Ernie's funeral?

100. What was the name of the one-time *Morecambe & Wise* writer who died only days before Ernie?

Pot Luck 1

Why not see how many of the following first set of 20 pot-luck questions, which all relate to Morecambe & Wise, you can answer correctly?

101. In which year did Morecambe & Wise sign with the agent Frank Pope?

102. In a sketch on *The Morecambe & Wise Christmas Show* in 1977, which actors from the cast of the classic Perry and Croft sitcom *Dad's Army* did Elton John supposedly find relaxing in a steam room in the BBC Television Centre?

103. In which year were Eric and Ernie both awarded the OBE?

104. How many years were Eric and Ernie officially a double act – 43, 44 or 45?

105. Which female singing trio did Eric nickname 'The Beatles' during their appearance on *The Morecambe & Wise Show* – the Andrews Sisters, the Beverley Sisters or the Kaye Sisters?

106. What was the name of the sculptor who created a large Arts Council-funded statue of Morecambe & Wise in 1977?

107. On which date did Eric and Ernie attend the unveiling of their wax effigies at Madame Tussauds in London – Thursday 10 February 1972, Friday 11 February 1972 or Saturday 12 February 1972?

108. Which television presenter did Eric once say his wax effigy resembled?

Gary Morecambe

Gary Morecambe is the son of Eric Morecambe; became a full-time writer in 1982. In *Memories of Eric*, he wrote:

'My father walked into the house, having just returned from BBC Television Centre and a visit to the studio hairdresser.

"Hi, Dad," I said, noticing the short back and sides. "I like the haircut."

"Good."

"It makes you look like Sean Connery."

"Yes. A very Shorn Connery."

As part of a promotional tour to launch my first book about my father, he and I went on *The Russell Harty Show*. During the on-air conversation I said to Russell that, with my father's second heart attack, I felt very much a part of it. My father dived in with, "Yes – he caused it."

End of any serious conversation.'

109. In a sketch that featured Elton John, what room number did a BBC receptionist say he should make his way to – 403, 404 or 405?

110. True or false: Eric and Ernie received the freedom of the City of London in 1972?

111. In which year did Kenneth Tynan profile Morecambe & Wise in the *Observer Magazine*?

112. What is the correct title of a screenplay that Morecambe & Wise were sent (and later rejected) in 1967?

113. What was the name of the American comedian whom Eric impersonated with the aid of a paper cup?

Bobby Ball

Bobby Ball and his comedy partner, Tommy Cannon, are one of Britain's funniest and most successful double acts. Here, Bobby recalls a memorable visit he and Tommy once made to Luton Town FC:

'Tommy and I were great fans of Eric and Ernie and one of the biggest highs of our career was when we were invited to Luton Town FC to visit some children there and Eric happened to be there. To meet one of our heroes, well, one can't explain the feeling. He greeted us and told us he was a great admirer of our comedy, which once again blew our minds. We went to meet the children and when we met them they were all having fizzy drinks in this room. At that time Tom and I were flying with our own television series every Saturday night on ITV, so this was my chance to show off in front of Eric! Lifting myself up to my full height (5ft 4in) I pulled my braces and shouted at the top of my voice: "Rock on, Tommy!"...Silence...not a murmur...the kids just looked at me with open mouths. Then Eric stepped forward and said, "No, this is how you do it, Bobby," and he put his glasses to one side of his face as he used to do and shouted: "Way-hay!" The kids fell about and it was then that I knew I was in the same room as a comic genius. He was truly a legend. And do you know what, not one swear word ever passed his lips. How times have changed!'

114. In a sketch which saw Eric as a stunt motorcyclist, what words were written on the back of his leather jacket?

115. In which year did Billy Marsh become Morecambe & Wise's agent?

116. What was the name of the children's comic that used to feature a cartoon strip called *Morecambe & Wise*?

117. In a Christmas edition of *The Morecambe & Wise Show*, what did Eric maintain Ernie's initials stood for?

118. Complete the following line that Eric used to say when requesting Ernie make him a hot beverage: '____ Ern.'

119. Which late member of the royal family reportedly once asked Eric how he did his famous trick with a paper bag and an imaginary ball?

120. In which year did Morecambe & Wise receive a posthumous BAFTA Fellowship award – 1999, 2000 or 2001?

Stage

Eric and Ernie first started working together by treading the boards, so why not see just how many of the following 50 questions in this section you can answer correctly on the subject of their stage credits?

121. At which theatre did Morecambe & Wise make their debut as a double act?

122. How long did Morecambe & Wise appear for at London's famous Windmill Theatre – one week, two weeks or three weeks?

123. At which theatre did Eric and Ernie first perform their 'Woody Woodpecker's Song' routine?

124. Complete the title of the touring review Eric and Ernie appeared in early in their careers: *Front Page* _____.

125. Complete the name of the theatre that Eric and Ernie appeared at in variety: Golders _____ Hippodrome.

126. Morecambe & Wise once appeared in a stage revue that had the initials TITS. But what was the full title of this production?

127. True or false: Eric and Ernie once appeared in a show called *Fig Leaves and Apple Sauce*?

128. True or false: the comedy duo once appeared in pantomime at the Little Theatre, Leicester?

129. Complete the title of the pantomime that Eric and Ernie performed in at the Grand Theatre, Brighton: *Jack* ____ ____ _____.

130. At which theatre did the actress Dame Flora Robson once make a special visit to see Eric and Ernie perform – Hulme Hippodrome, Lewisham Hippodrome or Shoreditch Empire?

131. True or false: Morecambe & Wise never appeared at the Morecambe Winter Gardens?

132. Complete the title of a pantomime that the double act appeared in at Dewsbury Empire: *Red* _____ _____.

133. At which West Midlands town did Morecambe & Wise appear in pantomime with Harry Secombe – Birmingham, Coventry or Wolverhampton?

134. Name the pantomime in which Morecambe & Wise appeared in during Christmas 1952 – *Cinderella, Dick Whittington* or *The Sleeping Beauty*.

135. True or false: Morecambe & Wise supported George Formby in a summer season in Blackpool?

136. How much would it have cost you to have purchased a ticket to sit in the stalls to see the double act in a week-long run at the Empire Theatre in West Hartlepool in the early 1950s – 1s/3d, 2s/3d or 3s/6d?

137. Complete the name of the theatre Eric and Ernie appeared at in the 1950s: Camberwell _____.

138. What was the surname of the puppeteers Paul and Peta, with whom Morecambe & Wise both appeared on variety bills and in summer season – Frost, Page or Roberts?

139. Name the toothy Liverpool comedian who appeared in summer season with Eric and Ernie in the northern resort of Blackpool during the 1950s?

140. At which British seaside resort was the duo appearing in summer season when they were offered their first television series of their own – Blackpool, Southport or Paignton?

141. At which theatre in Blackpool were Morecambe & Wise appearing when Eric's daughter, Gail, was born?

142. What was the name of the first theatre that Eric and Ernie played after their first-ever television series was broadcast?

143. What was the title of Eric and Ernie's 1957 summer season show – *Let's Celebrate*, *Let's Have Fun* or *Let's Party*?

144. True or false: Morecambe & Wise toured Australia for eight months in the late 1950s?

145. At which pier in Blackpool did Eric and Ernie appear for their 1959 summer season?

146. At which popular seaside resort did Eric and Little Ern appear in summer season in 1960?

147. Which magician was on the same bill as Morecambe & Wise at the Princess Theatre, Torquay, in the summer of 1961?

148. At which West End theatre did Eric and Ernie make their 1961 appearance in the *Royal Variety Show* – Her Majesty's, the London Palladium or the Prince of Wales?

149. In which year did Eric and Ernie play to packed houses during their summer season at the North Pier, Blackpool?

150. What was the title of the summer season show that Morecambe & Wise appeared in at the Wellington Pier Pavilion, Great Yarmouth, in 1964 – *Bring on the Show*, *Show Time 1964* or *The Show of 1964*?

151. What was the name of the well-known guitar player who appeared in a Great Yarmouth summer season with the comedy double act?

152. True or false: Albert J. Knight produced Morecambe & Wise's 1964 summer season?

David Benson

David Benson rose to fame following the incredible success of his debut solo show, *Think No Evil of Us: My Life with Kenneth Williams*. David recalls the time he saw Morecambe & Wise live on stage and later meeting Eric Morecambe at a book signing:

'The only time I met Eric Morecambe he gave me something very precious: a joke. No doubt he gave almost everyone he met their very own private Morecambe joke. From what I know of him he had a compulsion, an almost psychotic urge to make quips, to hear laughter. But what made this joke unusual was that he never even heard my laughter.

I should say that the first time I had seen Eric Morecambe in the flesh was in 1976, when I was 14, at the Alexandra Theatre, Birmingham. I am rather proud of the fact that the first time I ever went to the theatre by myself it was to see Eric and Ernie doing one of their live appearances in the 1970s. We got Ray Allen and Lord Charles, music from an ageing, silver-haired male pianist, a juggler of some sort and the Beverley Sisters.

The second half of the show belonged to Eric and Ernie. In the mid-1970s Morecambe & Wise were of course at the peak of their career. The show they performed that night contained material they must have performed thousands of times over the years and yet, magically, it all seemed fresh-minted, almost improvised. Eric in particular had the great gift for making everything he said seem like a spontaneous quip off the top of his head.

I shall never forget him flapping his hands in his trouser pockets with that far-away, "I'm not all there" look in his eyes, Ernie just watching him, the audience howling with laughter. It was a moment when time stood still; it could have gone on for 10 seconds or 10 minutes, that simple bit of business. Even now I cannot tell you WHY it was so funny. You just had to be there, I suppose.

A few years later I saw an advert in the *Birmingham Evening Mail* which informed the readers that Eric Morecambe would be signing copies of his first novel at Hudson's bookshop. I skipped A-level history that afternoon and headed into town. It was only when I got to the shop that I realised I was in trouble: the book cost £7.99 and I only had five pounds on me!'

Moving to the humour shelves I found an alternative selection, a mass market book of jokes and pictures called *The Morecambe & Wise Scrapbook*, price £1.75. Perfect.

I joined the long queue of fans, all clutching copies of Eric's new book, some even pretending to read it. A cow employed by the bookshop made her way up and down the line asking, "Have you got a copy of the book? Very good. Excuse me, do you have a copy of the book? No, madam, I'm sorry, he won't sign bus tickets. You must have a copy of the book. Do you have a copy of the book, young man?" she asked me. I pointed to my carrier bag. "Yes, I've got the book," I said, not strictly speaking lying. It was "the book" just not the correct book. Let's just say, it had all the right words but not necessarily in the right order!

Somewhere at the head of the line I heard laughter so I knew he must have arrived. After a long wait, with my heart thumping wildly, the queue rounded a bookshelf and there, just a few feet away, sat at a table was the real, actual Eric Morecambe, bald head, glasses, the lot. I noticed that he thanked every person whose book he signed, with an almost plaintive "Thank you very much for coming" as if they were old friends who had been to visit him in hospital.

When it was finally my turn I cleared my throat and made the short speech that I had been rehearsing in my head for the last fifteen minutes: "Mr. Morecambe, I'm very sorry but I can't afford your book…" Everyone laughed, including Eric Morecambe – but not the cow from the bookshop. If looks could kill!

"Would you mind signing this for me instead?" I pulled the cheap paperback out of my bag. "Not at all, I'd be delighted," he said. "What's your name?" He signed it and handed it back to me. "Thank you very much. Thank you for coming," he said.

When I got out onto the pavement I opened the book. He'd written: "To David - Save up! Eric Morecambe.'"

153. At which Manchester theatre did the legendary duo appear in the pantomime *The Sleeping Beauty* in 1964?

154. Prior to the opening, how much had Eric and Ernie's 1964 pantomime taken at the box office – £100,000, £200,000 or £300,000?

155. True or false: singer Edmund Hockridge did not appear with Morecambe & Wise on stage?

156. Morecambe & Wise appeared in a special gala show in America to mark the 80th birthday of which American composer and lyricist?

157. What was the name of the performer whose ventriloquist's act was the original inspiration for Eric and Ernie's own ventriloquist's routine?

158. In which year did Morecambe & Wise appear at the ABC Theatre, Great Yarmouth, in summer season?

159. What was the name of the East Midlands city that Eric and Ernie performed at on 10 December 1967 – Derby, Leicester or Nottingham?

160. How much did Morecambe & Wise's record-breaking second summer season run in Great Yarmouth make at the box office – £105,640, £110,660 or £115,000?

Did You Know?

If you had wanted to buy a souvenir programme for Morecambe & Wise's summer season show in 1967 it would have cost you 1s/-.

161. At which British seaside resort did Eric and Ernie first perform their ventriloquist's routine – Blackpool, Great Yarmouth or Torquay?

162. At which seaside theatre did the double act first appear following Eric's recovery from his first heart attack?

163. What did Eric jokingly call the live shows he and Ernie did in the 1970s?

164. True or false: Eric and Ernie appeared at Club Fiesta in Sheffield?

165. Morecambe & Wise appeared at which of the following venues on 15 and 16 October 1971 – ABC, Blackpool, ABC, Exeter or Alexandra Theatre, Birmingham?

166. How many Sunday concerts did Morecambe & Wise appear in at the Britannia Pier Theatre, Great Yarmouth, in 1975 – four, five or six?

167. In an advert on the back of a souvenir programme for one of the concerts in the 1970s, what type of bread did Eric and Eric endorse?

168. True or false: Eric's son, Gary, used to help sell merchandise in the foyer of certain live show appearances that Morecambe & Wise made during the 1970s?

169. Complete the name of the venue Morecambe & Wise appeared at: Preston _____.

170. True or false: Morecambe & Wise appeared in four Sunday concerts in the 1970s staged at the Pavilion Theatre, Cromer?

Radio

Before television finally came knocking, Morecambe & Wise broadcast to the nation on the radio. But how many of the following 20 questions in this section can you answer correctly on the duo's various radio credits?

171. What was the title of Eric and Ernie's first-ever radio series?

172. What was the name of the actor, best-known for playing a policeman called Korky in the classic sitcom *Sykes!*, who was a member of the cast of Eric and Ernie's first radio series?

173. From which northern town was Morecambe & Wise's first radio series broadcast – Leeds, Liverpool or Manchester?

174. A radio show in which the duo performed was broadcast from the Shepherd's Bush Empire on 23 October 1951, but which of the following one-time *Goon Show* performers was top of the bill – Spike Milligan, Harry Secombe or Peter Sellers?

175. True or false: Morecambe & Wise first took part in the radio series *Blackpool Night* in 1950?

176. On which date did Eric and Ernie first take part in the radio show *Henry Hall's Guest Night* – 26 February 1954, 26 March 1954 or 26 April 1954?

177. Complete the title of the radio show which Morecambe & Wise performed on: *Workers'* _____.

178. How many editions of the radio series *Youth Must Have Its Fling!* did the comedy double act take part in?

179. How many editions of the radio series *Variety Fanfare* did Morecambe & Wise take part in – 43, 44 or 45?

180. True or false: Eric and Ernie once took part in a radio show called *Morecambe Illuminations*?

181. In which year did the duo first star in a radio series entitled *The Morecambe & Wise Show*?

182. Morecambe & Wise performed in a radio show on 11 June 1961, what was the title – *Seaside Fun*, *Seaside Nights* or *Seaside Special*?

183. On which BBC Radio 4 programme first broadcast in 1969 did Eric recall his personal wartime experiences?

184. True or false: Eric and Ernie once took part in a radio show special entitled *Morecambe & Wise Sing Flanagan and Allen*?

185. Complete the title of the radio show Morecambe & Wise made in 1974: *Eric and Ernie's ____ __ ____*.

186. What was the name of the performer who took part in a radio sketch with Eric and Ernie and who was well known for impersonating animals and birds?

187. In which year did the comedy duo record *The Morecambe & Wise Christmas Show* for BBC Radio 2 – 1975, 1976 or 1977?

188. True or false: although the actress, singer and dancer Anita Harris worked with Eric and Ernie on television, she never actually took part in a radio show with them?

189. On which date was the last edition of the radio version of *The Eric Morecambe and Ernie Wise Show* originally broadcast – 25 March 1978, 26 March 1978 or 27 March 1978?

190. True or false: Ernie Wise took part in a radio show called *Wise on the Wireless*?

Phil Collinge and Andy Lord

Phil Collinge and Andy Lord have written for a host of TV and radio comedy shows. They still treasure the rejection letter they once received for a piece of work that was criticised for reading like 'a Morecambe & Wise script':

'To write something nice about Morecambe & Wise is easy – in fact, it would be very difficult to write anything else! Eric and Ernie weren't just liked by the British public, they were loved and this extraordinary popularity was due in no small part (can we say "no small part"?) to the exceptional quality of their scripted material.

From a writer's point of view, one of the remarkable things about a Morecambe & Wise script is how elements of the performers' real personalities were reflected in their stage personas. Eric and Ernie always claimed that there was a lot of themselves in their shows and this "personalisation" was illustrated to great effect in the Eddie Braben scripted masterpieces set in the boys' fictional flat – bestowing on the viewer a feeling that they had witnessed a chapter from the boys' everyday life rather than being exposed to a staged event.

These "mini sit-coms" treated us to a brief glimpse of the boys' supposed home life, and were portrayed in direct contrast to other segments of the show that mimicked the traditional variety theatres of their youth. The scenes in the flat saw the boys relaxed, in conversation, in heated discussion ... and even in bed together! Of course, we all knew that Eric and Ernie didn't really live together (or did we?) but these scenarios, written by Braben, ingeniously emphasised the boys' closeness and innocence while allowing the viewer to indulge their voyeuristic tendencies and sneak a peek at the "private lives" of their comedy heroes.

And what private lives they were! Everyone has their favourite "flat moment", but who can forget the scene where the police car screamed past the bedroom – sirens blaring, only for Eric to casually glance behind the curtains and exclaim: "He'll not sell much ice-cream going at that speed."

There's no answer to that!'

Television

Morecambe & Wise, of course, achieved their biggest success on television and it is this work that most of their fans know and love the best. But just how much do you really know about Eric and Ernie's various television credits? To find out, why not try attempting to answer the 200 questions in this section?

191. In which year did Morecambe & Wise make their first appearance on BBC television?

192. Complete the title of the television show that Eric and Ernie appeared on in December 1953: *Pantomime* _____.

193. What was the title of Morecambe & Wise's first-ever television series of their own?

194. How many editions of Eric and Ernie's first-ever television series did Len Fincham and Laurie Wyman write?

195. What was the name of the BBC boss who gave the duo their first television series?

196. At what time did the BBC broadcast Eric and Ernie's first series – 7.30pm, 8.30pm or 9.30pm?

197. True or false: the singer Alma Cogan appeared in Morecambe & Wise's first-ever television series?

198. What was the name of the former *Coronation Street* actress who appeared in Eric and Ernie's first television series for the BBC?

199. Which of the following *Carry On* film actors appeared in Morecambe & Wise's first BBC television series – Bernard Bresslaw, Kenneth Connor or Sid James?

200. Where was the duo's first-ever TV series broadcast from?

201. On which date did the double act's first television series get broadcast – 21 April 1954, 22 April 1954 or 23 April 1954?

202. True or false: Eric and Ernie's first-ever television series for the BBC was broadcast weekly?

203. Complete the well-known review that Eric and Ernie received for their first-ever own television show – 'Definition of the week: TV set – the box they _____ _____ _ _____ __'.

204. What was the name of the then future writer of the BBC sitcom *Till Death Us Do Part* who wrote material for Morecambe & Wise's appearances on *The Winifred Atwell Show* in 1956?

205. What was the title of the fast-paced revue that Morecambe & Wise presented for the BBC in 1957?

206. Complete the title of the programme on which Eric and Ernie made an early TV appearance: *The Bob _____ Hour*.

207. How many appearances on Val Parnell's *Sunday Night at the London Palladium* did Morecambe & Wise make in 1960 – 10, 11 or 12?

208. What was the name of the comedy series in which the BBC hoped that Eric and Ernie would appear during the early 1960s?

209. What was the subtitle of the double act's television shows made for ATV – *Two's Company*, *Two is a Crime* or *Two of a Kind*?

210. True or false: Eric and Ernie's first-ever television series for ATV was broadcast from the Chiswick Empire?

211. How many editions were made of the duo's first television series for ATV – six, nine or twelve?

212. How many editions of Eric and Ernie's ATV shows lasted 30 minutes each – 25, 35 or 45?

213. True or false: the main producer and director of Morecambe & Wise's television shows for ATV was Colin Clews?

Andrew Collins

Andrew Collins is a scriptwriter, journalist and broadcaster, who has written for soaps and music magazines, and regularly appears on TV documentaries. He recalls a season of goodwill during which Eric and Ernie's guests included Hannah Gordon:

'It's Christmas Day, 1973. Three generations of my family are gathered around the television in our brown-and-orange living room at Winsford Way in Northampton to witness *The Morecambe & Wise Christmas Special* on BBC1, now as well established as *The Queen's Speech*, which my Nan will have made us watch in the afternoon. No such coercion is required for Morecambe & Wise. I'm eight years old and already an avid fan – although I'd come to appreciate Eric and Ernie's work far more profoundly in adult life, partly through the historical and social context of their 1970s heyday, but mainly because I found that their routines still make me laugh. Of all the delights served up in those Christmas Specials – from Shirley Bassey to Angela Rippon – it's a sketch which featured Hannah Gordon singing that remains my most vivid memory, and it takes me right back to being eight years old again.

The stage is set for the usual tomfoolery, with Ms Gordon singing in the shadow of a huge, full-size prop windmill. Within about two bars of the song, which I knew from hearing it at Nan's on *The Jimmy Young Show*, Eric and Ernie are sneaking on behind a pointless twig to mend the stopped blade in their brown overalls, and Ernie – or a stuntman substituted during a cutaway to the valiantly professional Ms Gordon – is whisked off the ground. But this shtick is not what has cemented the routine to my mind. It's when Eric accidentally switches the wind machine to "Typhoon" and Hannah Gordon's evening dress is blown off. At my young age, I was so shocked to see her in a petticoat! Eric and Ernie manfully try to cover her dignity, but she walks off in the wrong direction and we see her in her underwear in full view. Even though I was too young to be actually aroused by the sight of it, it did disturb me deeply, and I've never forgotten it. It all seems so tame now, but not in 1973. It may seem odd to have chosen a moment that actually kind of upset me (on Hannah Gordon's behalf, you understand – I was a budding gentleman!), but that's the lasting power of Morecambe & Wise. This was classic television, built to last. I have viewed the clip again recently, and it's the bit where she slides down a broken prop gate that makes me laugh the most. And I'm old enough now to be aroused by the petticoat!'

214. On what day of the week was Morecambe & Wise's first ATV series broadcast?

215. What was the name of the trade union that Eric and Ernie both belonged to which meant that the duo could continue with their first series despite Equity being on strike?

216. Morecambe & Wise's third series for ATV gained which position in the top 20 television ratings in the year 1963 – number one, number two or number three?

217. How many editions of *The Morecambe & Wise Show* made for ATV had a running time of 35 minutes?

218. On which date was The Beatles' appearance on *The Morecambe & Wise Show* first broadcast – 17 April 1964, 18 April 1964 or 19 April 1964?

219. What did Eric jokingly call Ringo Starr during The Beatles' appearance on a Morecambe & Wise show made for ATV – Bingo, Bongo or Bonzo?

220. Which song did Eric and Ernie and The Beatles perform together during the group's appearance on *The Morecambe & Wise Show*?

221. True or false: Morecambe & Wise had an annual Christmas television show when working for ATV?

222. In a parody of *77 Sunset Strip*, what was the number of the building which the double act were clearly seen to be standing outside – 56, 66 or 76?

223. In a sketch on one of their ATV shows, what battle were Eric and Ernie seen to be re-enacting with toy solders?

224. How many editions of Morecambe & Wise's ATV shows lasted 60 minutes – 10, 11 or 12?

225. True or false: in a sketch which saw the duo taking part in a boxing match, the referee was the only person to get hurt?

226. Which terrestrial television channel broadcast many of Eric and Ernie's ATV shows in the late 1990s – BBC1, BBC2 or Channel 4?

227. In a parody of the television game show *Take Your Pick*, what did Morecambe & Wise call their version of the show?

228. What did Eric and Ernie nickname a one-time co-writer of their television show, Dick Hills – Dandy Dick, Father Christmas or the Laughing Policeman?

229. True or false: Ernie played the role of Cleopatra in a sketch made for one of the duo's ATV shows?

230. In a sketch in which Eric pretended to be his own cousin in order to impress a member of the opposite sex, what name did he call himself – Bernard, Bert or Conrad?

231. What was the name of the ATV 1960s quiz show hosted by Shaw Taylor which Morecambe & Wise parodied in a memorable sketch?

232. What was the name of the media company which released videos in the early 1990s that featured classic sketches from Eric and Ernie's ATV shows?

233. Which of the following series that Morecambe & Wise made for ATV did Millicent Martin appear in – series four, series five or series six?

234. What did Ed Sullivan mistakenly call the comedy double act when they made their first appearance on his American television series?

235. What was the name of the actress who went on to star in the BBC sitcom *Keeping Up Appearances* who Eric and Ernie both met while recording a television show in New York?

236. How many editions of *The Morecambe & Wise Show* did Eric and Ernie make for ATV?

237. In a sketch made for an ATV show that was set in a Chinese restaurant, what English food did Eric prefer to order instead?

238. How many series did Morecambe & Wise make for ATV – five, six or seven?

239. What was the title given to the American version of Eric and Ernie's last-ever ATV series?

240. On what date was Morecambe & Wise's last-ever show for ATV first broadcast in Britain – 29 March 1968, 30 March 1968 or 31 March 1968?

241. How many times did Eric and Ernie perform their judo routine on American television – three, four or five times?

242. True or false: although Morecambe & Wise's last ATV series was screened in America in colour, it was only screened in monochrome in Britain?

243. True or false: Sammy Davis Jr appeared on an ATV edition of *The Morecambe & Wise Show*?

244. What was the name of the head of variety at BBC television who signed Morecambe & Wise to the corporation in 1968?

245. How many main editions of *The Morecambe & Wise Show* did Eric and Ernie make for the BBC when they moved back to that broadcaster in 1968?

246. What was the name of the actor who became Morecambe & Wise's first major star guest on their return to BBC television?

247. How many television series did Morecambe & Wise make for the BBC from 1968 onwards?

248. On which date did the BBC first broadcast Eric and Ernie's first edition of *The Morecambe & Wise Show* – 1 September 1968, 2 September 1968 or 3 September 1968?

249. True or false: actor Sir John Gielgud once turned down the opportunity to appear on *The Morecambe & Wise Show*?

250. Christmas shows aside, what was the running time of the majority of Eric and Ernie's BBC television shows?

Jimmy Cricket

Jimmy Cricket worked at Butlins holiday camps before stage and television fame finally came to the comedian. He had a memorable television series made for ITV by Central Television entitled *And There's More*:

'Morecambe & Wise were one of our best-loved comedy duos. Sadly I never got to meet Eric, but I did meet Ernie several times in his latter years and found him stimulating and riveting company.

My other link to "The Boys" was with a guy called Eddie Braben, who wrote all their golden shows for the BBC. Eddie wrote a radio series for me called *Jimmy's Cricket Team* in the 1990s. Eddie is one of our best comedy writers ever and I am happy to report that he is living in blissful happiness in north Wales with his lovely wife Deidre, still counting the cash he received from the Eric and Ernie shows!

I suppose one of my most favourite sketches was when Eric looked up at the window and there was a gigantic blow up of King Kong. He turned to Ernie and shouted: "Have we got a new window cleaner?"'

251. How much of Morecambe & Wise's 1968 series remains in the archives – only part of one edition, two editions or three editions?

252. In which year did Morecambe & Wise host *Christmas Night with the Stars* – 1968, 1969 or 1970?

253. Following their return to television after Eric's first heart attack, who became the musical director on *The Morecambe & Wise Show*?

254. What percentage of the population is said to have watched *The Morecambe & Wise Christmas Show* in 1969?

255. True or false: singer Moira Anderson appeared on an edition of *The Morecambe & Wise Show* on 23 August 1969?

256. True or false: Dale Winton's actress mother, Sheree Winton, made a guest appearance on *The Morecambe & Wise Show*?

257. What was the name of the actress best known for her role in the film *Carry On Screaming* who appeared in an edition of *The Morecambe & Wise Show* in February 1970?

258. True or false: Edward Woodward appeared on *The Morecambe & Wise Show Christmas Show* in 1970?

259. Name the one-time *Blue Peter* gardener who appeared on an edition of *The Morecambe & Wise Show*.

260. For extra comic effect, what vital element was left out of Morecambe & Wise's 'Singin' in the Rain' routine?

261. What was the name of the first-ever host of the talent show *Opportunity Knocks* who appeared on *The Morecambe & Wise Show* in 1974?

262. Which singer, best known as the original forces' sweetheart, appeared on *The Morecambe & Wise Christmas Show* in 1972?

263. What was the name of the 10-foot-tall ventriloquist's doll that once appeared on *The Morecambe & Wise Show*?

264. What was the name of the *Sky at Night* presenter who once appeared on *The Morecambe & Wise Show*?

265. Which actor played King Richard in the sketch 'The Adventures of King Richard'?

266. What was the name of the member of the royal family who was approached to appear on *The Morecambe & Wise Christmas Show* in 1972?

267. True or false: Eric and Ernie appeared on the television show *Jim'll Fix It*?

268. Complete the title of this Morecambe & Wise compilation show: *I _____ ____ Morecambe & Wise*.

269. Which actor, best known for playing the role of Robin Hood, appeared on *The Morecambe & Wise Show* in 1970?

270. What was the name of the nautical-based sketch that Arthur Lowe appeared in on *The Morecambe & Wise Show*?

271. True or false: comedian Dick Emery was too ill to make an appearance on *The Morecambe & Wise Christmas Show* in 1971?

272. What was the running time of *The Morecambe & Wise Christmas Show* in 1971?

273. True or false: in 1972 Morecambe & Wise only made a Christmas special, and not any other editions of their television series?

274. Unhappy with the catering arrangements while rehearsing for his appearance on *The Morecambe & Wise Show*, what did Robert Morley have delivered to the rehearsal room?

275. In a sketch that featured the actress Dame Flora Robson, what role did Eric play – a butler, gardener or chauffeur?

276. What was the subtitle of the 1973 BBC *Omnibus* documentary about Morecambe & Wise?

277. True or false: actor Kenneth Williams appeared in *The Morecambe & Wise Show* in 1973?

278. How many BAFTA awards did Morecambe & Wise win for their television work between 1963 and 1977 – four, five or six?

279. Which actress played Empress Josephine in the sketch 'Napoleon and Josephine' on an edition of Eric and Ernie's show for the BBC?

280. What is the name of the *Dad's Army* actor who played a shop assistant in 'The Health Food Shop' sketch in a BBC show Morecambe & Wise made – James Beck, Bill Pertwee or Frank Williams?

281. What role did Eric play in the sketch 'The Adventures of Robin Hood'?

282. Which legendary Hollywood song and dance man was a huge fan of Eric and Ernie's 'Singin' in the Rain' routine?

283. Who was the one-time host of *Question Time*, known for wearing a bow tie, who made an appearance on *The Morecambe & Wise Show*?

284. What was the title of the sketch in which actor Sir John Mills played the role of Major Faversham?

285. In the famous sketch 'Antony and Cleopatra', first made for a BBC edition of *The Morecambe & Wise Show*, what role did Little Ern give himself to play?

286. Which well-known actor played Casanova in a sketch called 'Lust Over London'?

287. What is the name of the one-time radio DJ who used to present the radio show *Open House* and who played the role of the Red Baron in a much-loved Morecambe & Wise sketch?

288. Which actress first appeared on *The Morecambe & Wise Show* fresh from acting in the series *The Forsyte Saga*?

289. In the 'Red Baron' sketch, what role did Ernie play?

290. True or false: writer Ron McDonnell provided additional material for certain shows Morecambe & Wise made for the BBC?

291. What was the name of the fictitious playwright who supposedly lived in the same block of flats as Eric and Ernie and once appeared in a sketch?

Did You Know?

Television presenter Michael Aspel made a series of very funny but sadly never broadcast trailers with Eric and Ernie for *The Morecambe & Wise Show* at the BBC.

292. How many editions did the double act make of *The Morecambe & Wise Show* for their seventh series at the BBC – 12, 13 or 14?

293. Which actor (now deceased), who appeared in the drama series *Upstairs Downstairs* and *The Professionals*, made a guest appearance on the 1975 edition of *The Morecambe & Wise Christmas Show*?

294. True or false: chat-show host Michael Parkinson presented a Morecambe & Wise compilation special during Christmas 1974?

295. What was the title of the song which Eric and Ernie performed with actress Michelle Dotrice in a sketch?

296. Which song did Eric and Ernie perform with Lena Zavaroni?

297. What did Eric do at the very end of the 'Singin' in the Rain' routine?

298. In a Latin American routine that featured Morecambe & Wise and Vanessa Redgrave, what happened to Eric's maracas?

299. At the end of the 'Slaughter on Fifth Avenue' routine, what happened to Ernie?

300. In the 'South Pacific' routine, what song did Morecambe & Wise and their guests perform?

301. In a sketch which featured Eric and Ernie dressed as two reindeers, what role did Bruce Forsyth briefly play?

302. In a classic flat sketch, which female fictional character was Eric supposedly watching as she hung out her underwear on the washing line?

303. In a routine that featured Eric and Ernie dancing with a group of male dancers in top hat and tails, what did the dancers do throughout the routine?

304. In a short sketch in which Ernie was supposedly being knighted by the Queen, what could be seen dangling from the sword as it was raised from his shoulders?

305. True or false: actor Roger Moore played the role of Miles Behind in a television show Morecambe & Wise made for the BBC?

306. In the classic 'Singin' in the Rain' routine, what happened after Ernie threw his umbrella up in the air?

307. At the end of 'The Stripper' routine, what electrical object does Eric accidentally chop with a large cleaver?

308. What television theme tune extract did Eric make his entrance to in the 'Antony and Cleopatra' sketch?

309. In a sketch on *The Morecambe & Wise Show*, what did Eric say he thought Arthur Negus' second name was?

310. Complete the title of the book Eric was reading in bed in a flat sketch – *Wind ___ ___ _____.*

311. True or false: Eric made a guest appearance on Eric Sykes' sitcom *Sykes!*?

312. In a sketch, what did Eric say he thought the initials of the company name EMI stood for?

313. How many grapefruits did Eric halve in 'The Stripper' routine?

314. How long did it take to film the famous 'Singin' in the Rain' routine – 20, 40 or 60 minutes?

315. What was the name of the actor who played the vicar in the sitcom *Steptoe & Son* and often appeared in sketches on *The Morecambe & Wise Show* on the BBC?

316. What was the title of the song that Tom Jones sang and Eric and Ernie danced to in a famous sketch on *The Morecambe & Wise Show*?

317. What is the name of the actor who played Fred Quilley in the classic sitcom *Hi-de-Hi!* who was one of the studio audience warm-up men on *The Morecambe & Wise Show*?

318. Which prison is situated close to where Eric and Ernie used to rehearse for their BBC television shows?

319. What mispronounced version of Elton John's name did Eric once give during a sketch?

320. At what time of night was the 1976 edition of *The Morecambe & Wise Christmas Show* broadcast?

321. True or false: entertainer Larry Grayson appeared in Eric and Ernie's 1976 Christmas special?

322. On what date was the 'South Pacific' routine recorded for *The Morecambe & Wise Christmas Show* in 1977 – Thursday 8 December 1977, Friday 9 December 1977 or Saturday 10 December 1977?

323. How many people are said to have watched *The Morecambe & Wise Christmas Show* in 1977 – 28,835,000, 28,850,000 or 28,865,000?

324. What were the names of all the male guests who took part in the famous 'South Pacific' routine in the 1977 Christmas special?

Richard Digance

Surviving all trends in comedy and music, Richard Digance continues to remain one of Britain's most popular entertainers:

'Like most British people of a certain age, I was brought up on Morecambe & Wise. They were there for as long as I can remember, as a schoolkid making me laugh through boring Christmas Days after the Queen had successfully negotiated her autocue for another year. Strangely I didn't appreciate the value of Ernie Wise until I was in show business myself. The stooge, the straight man, without whom Eric couldn't fire his bullets of hilarity and the man who held the timing together. I met Ernie when he was doing a gardening programme and for me it was great to be in the presence of a comedy genius, half of the greatest duo the world has ever seen. They made me laugh more than Abbott and Costello, Laurel and Hardy, and as a young kid growing up in the East End I loved them as much as Geoff Hurst and Martin Peters.

Did I ever meet them? Yes, but only on a few occasions and I only worked with them the once at a charity show, which I seem to remember being at a nightclub in Luton in the shadows of the M1 motorway. Jim Davidson told me that night I would never meet any others more professional or alluring to an audience, and he was absolutely right. It will always remain an honour.'

325. Name the characters Eric and Ernie played in a sketch that sent-up the American television series *Starsky and Hutch*.

326. What type of car did Morecambe & Wise and the 'baddies' both drive in the 'Starsky and Hutch' send-up sketch?

327. On which date did Eric and Ernie record the last-ever BBC television show of their own in front of a studio audience – Sunday 11 December 1977, Monday 12 December 1977 or Tuesday 13 December 1977?

328. At what time was *The Morecambe & Wise Christmas Show* broadcast in 1977?

329. True or false: Eric once jokingly said the letters 'BBC' stood for Bring Back Comedy?

330. In which year did Morecambe & Wise move over to Thames Television?

331. Which television company broadcast a Variety Club tribute to Morecambe & Wise in Birmingham during 1978?

332. How many editions of *The Morecambe & Wise Show* did Eric and Ernie make for Thames Television – 32, 33 or 34?

333. Which actor who co-starred in the LWT sitcom *Two's Company* appeared in the duo's first special for Thames Television?

334. What is the name of the actress from the BBC sitcom *As Times Goes By* who appeared on a Morecambe & Wise Thames Television special?

335. What is the name of the producer and director of Morecambe & Wise's first-ever Christmas special for Thames Television – Keith Beckett, Peter Frazer-Jones or Dennis Kirkland?

336. Where are the studios at which Eric and Ernie made their Thames Television shows?

337. Name the performer who was best known for his role as chairman on *The Good Old Days* who appeared in a special made by Morecambe & Wise for Thames Television.

338. In which year did the former British Prime Minister Harold Wilson appear in a Christmas version of *The Morecambe & Wise Show* for Thames – 1978, 1979 or 1980?

339. What was the name of the *Rising Damp* actor who appeared on Morecambe & Wise's first-ever Christmas special for Thames Television?

340. Complete the name of the actress, who also appeared in sketches on *The Benny Hill Show*, who took part in Morecambe & Wise's 1978 Christmas special for Thames – _____ Dawson.

341. From which stage school were children recruited to appear on the Christmas show Eric and Ernie made in 1978?

342. In the 'Fabulous Forties' sketch made for a Thames Christmas special, what characters did Morecambe & Wise play when they supposedly met Winston Churchill?

343. Which of the following female newsreaders did the double act once pretend they had on one of their Christmas shows for Thames – Anna Ford, Sue Lawley or Moira Stuart?

344. In a routine that involved Ernie conducting the Syd Lawrence Orchestra, what problem did Eric experience while attempting to play the piano?

345. In a pet shop sketch, what did Eric keep doing to a pretend parrot?

346. True or false: Rex Grey acted as one of the choreographers on Eric and Ernie's first Christmas show for Thames?

Graham McCann

Graham McCann is primarily a biographer and critic. He has contributed articles to several newspapers. He wrote a critically acclaimed biography of Eric and Ernie entitled *Morecambe & Wise*. He says:

'I would hate for younger people to think that Morecambe & Wise only attracted such a huge and loyal following simply because there were fewer TV channels from which to choose. Great performers, with great scripts and great producers, will attract big audiences no matter how many channels are on offer. Morecambe & Wise really earned their success, and they genuinely knew how to entertain a nation.

I grew up watching them on TV. I also saw them live. They never disappointed. Eric was a charmingly powerful and endlessly inventive comic force. Ernie was a kind and very clever comic feed as well as an inveterate "cheerer-upper". As a double act, they did not just make you laugh – they also made you care. It was a privilege to be entertained by them, and it is impossible to forget them.'

347. In a flat sketch in the 1978 Christmas show, what did Eric do to a television set when it was announced that Des O'Connor would be in the next programme?

348. Name the Australian entertainer whom Eric impersonated on a Christmas edition of *The Morecambe & Wise Show*.

349. In Ernie's version of the play *Hamlet* made for a Christmas show, which actor played the title role?

350. In a pet shop sketch made for one of Eric and Ernie's Christmas shows for Thames, what did Eric keep doing to a bowl that contained a pretend goldfish?

351. Eric played a live version of which cartoon cat in a sketch for a Thames Television show?

352. What is the name of the host of the long-running game show *Through the Keyhole* who appeared on the Christmas edition of *The Morecambe & Wise Show* on 25 December 1979?

353. True or false: Eamonn Andrews once appeared on a Christmas special made by Eric and Ernie for Thames Television?

354. Which male cast member from the classic radio comedy series *Round the Horne* appeared on *The Morecambe & Wise Show* on 10 September 1980?

355. In which year was Eric and Ernie's first full television series for Thames broadcast?

356. Who was the original host of *Blankety Blank* who appeared in an edition of the comedy double act's first series for Thames?

357. Which actor, who played Obi-Wan Kenobi in the original *Star Wars* trilogy, appeared on Eric and Ernie's Christmas show in 1980?

358. In a sketch on a Christmas special that Morecambe & Wise made for Thames Television, what present did Jill Gascoigne buy for Ernie – a hat, wig or wig stand?

359. In a sketch in which Eric was supposedly suffering from laryngitis, what did he use to communicate with his doctor?

360. In his adaptation of *Hamlet*, what role did Ernie play in the sketch which was part of a Christmas special made for Thames?

361. In a Christmas edition of *The Morecambe & Wise Show* which included Jill Gascoigne as a guest, what did Eric and Ernie give to the actress as a Christmas present?

362. Actress Diane Keen, best known for appearing in the sitcom *The Cuckoo Waltz*, appeared on *The Morecambe & Wise Show* on which date in September 1981 – 14, 15 or 16?

363. How many viewers are said to have watched Morecambe & Wise's Christmas show in 1981?

364. In the sketch entitled 'Captain Blood' which of the following sitcom actors played the title role – Ralph Bates, Richard Briers or Patrick Cargill?

365. Which one-time footballer appeared in an Atari advert with Morecambe & Wise in the early 1980s?

366. What was the name of the actress who played Ronnie Barker's daughter in the classic sitcom *Porridge* and who appeared on *The Morecambe & Wise Show* on 8 December 1982?

367. Which retired boxer, also known for appearing in adverts for a well-known aftershave, appeared on *The Morecambe & Wise Show*?

Did You Know?

A reporter commenting to Eric that he would have to '...take it easy for a bit' after leaving hospital after heart surgery received the following reply from the comedian: 'Well, if I can get a bit, I'll take it, easy'.

368. Name the racing driver who appeared in an advert with Morecambe & Wise for Texaco.

369. In a Thames Television edition of *The Morecambe & Wise Show*, which song from the musical *Chicago* did Eric and Ernie perform with the former actress Suzanne Danielle?

370. At the end of many editions of the double act's Thames Television shows, what was Eric often seen wearing?

371. Name the Thames Television special in which the double act recalled their early days of touring the theatres.

372. What is the name of the actor who plays Rodney Blackstock in the ITV soap *Emmerdale*, who appeared in Morecambe & Wise's last-ever Christmas special?

373. What is the name of the actor, best known for having played the role of Kato in the *Pink Panther* films, who appeared on Morecambe & Wise's last-ever Christmas show?

374. Who was the producer and director of Morecambe & Wise's last-ever television series?

375. True or false: Eric and Ernie's last Christmas show for Thames included a Keystone Cops routine?

376. True or false: both Morecambe and Wise once appeared on the Thames Television children's show *Rainbow*?

377. Complete the title of the children's show that Morecambe & Wise briefly hosted: _____ *Play*.

378. How many viewers are said to have watched a repeat showing of the 1977 Christmas Special on Christmas night 1993?

379. Which London store played a loop of two classic routines from *The Morecambe & Wise Show* as part of its Christmas window display in 1993?

380. In a list of the top 100 British television programmes compiled in 2000, at which number did the British Film Institute place *The Morecambe & Wise Show*?

381. What sketch did UKTV Gold viewers vote as their greatest Morecambe & Wise moment in a special 2007 compilation programme?

382. How many *Royal Variety Shows* did Morecambe & Wise appear in – four, five or six?

383. When someone coughed on *The Morecambe & Wise Show*, what football team name did Eric usually call out?

384. Which Morecambe & Wise sketch did comedienne Victoria Wood say was the best sketch of all time?

Billy Pearce

Yorkshire-born, award-winning comedian Billy Pearce has broken box office records at a number of theatres for summer season and pantomime. Here, he shares with us his thoughts on what Morecambe & Wise mean to him:

'I remember the "Boom Oo Ya-ta-ta-ta" routine and have done a similar routine in my own shows with the likes of Russell Watson, John Inman (bless him!) and The Osmonds.

I grew up with Morecambe & Wise and, like everyone else, loved them. In fact I have a collection of Christmas shows and we all sat and watched a couple of them the other night. I had the pleasure of meeting Mrs Morecambe at a Water Rats ball and was overawed!'

385. True or false: Paul and Linda McCartney both appeared in a sketch together on *The Morecambe & Wise Show*?

386. What object did Eric tend to have with him in the famous bed sketches in order to help retain his masculinity?

387. True or false: Eric used a Dictaphone to record his ideas for new sketches for *The Morecambe & Wise Show*?

388. Name the Morecambe & Wise compilation shows that Thames Television made for ITV in the late 1990s.

389. What two words did Eric usually say as he entered the set during one of Ernie's famous plays?

390. True or false: Eric originally objected to the idea of the bed sketches in *The Morecambe & Wise Show*?

Eric and Ernie Live

In the 1970s, Morecambe & Wise's live stage act was filmed for archiving purposes and was never originally meant to be broadcast on television. However, an edited version of this film was later broadcast on British television and released on VHS video. This section features 20 questions based on this rare film footage.

391. At which venue was this film recorded?

392. Who provided musical backing for Morecambe & Wise during this and their various other stage show appearances in the 1970s?

393. True or false: despite its popularity, Eric and Ernie did not perform their ventriloquist's routine at this particular performance?

394. Which American singer did Ernie impersonate while singing 'That's Why The Lady is a Tramp' during the show?

395. What instrument does Ernie teach Eric to use during the show?

396. Complete the title of a popular Morecambe & Wise routine which the double act performed during this show – 'The Swiss _____ Dance'.

397. Complete the title of a number that Eric and Ernie sang and danced to during the show – 'Pretty _____'.

398. True or false: Des O'Connor made a guest appearance with the comedy double act during this special show?

399. During a question-and-answer session held by the duo towards the end of the performance, which famous Morecambe & Wise joke did a woman in the audience request Eric to tell in full?

400. During the show, how long did Eric say he and Ernie had been working together as a double act?

401. Which song did Morecambe & Wise end the show with?

402. Which of the following people staged this show – Johnny Ammonds, Tudor Davies or Graham Stephenson?

403. Who produced the film of this show?

404. Which company made the original film of this show – Delta Film Productions, Delta Film and Television or Delta Sound?

405. Which television company broadcast an edited version of this film on ITV?

406. In which year was this film first broadcast on television?

407. How long was the running length of the edited version of this film broadcast on television – 60 minutes, 120 minutes or 150 minutes?

408. Which company later released this film on video?

409. How long is the video version of this film?

410. What was the original video BBFC certificate when it was released – U, PG or 12?

Wayne Dobson

The Leicester-born magician runs his own company with his wife and still continues to perform. He says:

'Some people say funny things, and some people say things funny, however, very few people have both of these qualities; Morecambe & Wise were one of the very few!'

The Sweeney

Always relishing the opportunity to try something different, Eric Morecambe and Ernie Wise were delighted when the opportunity came up for them to both appear in a special episode of the gritty police drama *The Sweeney*. In this section there are 20 questions that all relate to the special episode of this series they appeared in.

411. Which two production companies made this series?

412. What was the title of the episode in which Morecambe & Wise appeared?

413. On which date was this episode first broadcast on ITV – 22 November 1978, 23 November 1978 or 24 November 1978?

414. What are the names of the two actors who played the characters of Regan and Carter?

415. Which of the two main actors in the series suggested to Eric and Ernie that they appeared in an episode of the drama?

416. True or false: Morecambe & Wise played themselves in this episode?

417. Which actor played Detective Chief Inspector Frank Haskins in this series?

418. What is the name of the actor who played the role of Bellcourt?

419. What was the title of the current affairs programme Regan was seen watching in part of this episode?

420. Which actress, who went on to appear in the sitcom *Bread*, played a neighbour in this episode?

421. True or false: Mike Vardy directed this special episode?

422. What were the names of the two writers of this special episode?

423. Who were the two executive producers on this series?

424. Which of the following number plates was on the camper van featured in this special episode – NDV 655P, NDV 656P or NDV 657P?

Paul Welsh

Paul Welsh was awarded the MBE for his services to film industry preservation and for acting as chairman of the campaigns to save Elstree Studios.

'I remember going down to ATV in Borehamwood to get the autographs of The Beatles who were appearing on Eric and Ernie's shows. Sadly, I later swapped them and I guess they would be worth a couple of thousand pounds today!

I invited Eric Morecambe to one of our early Elstree Film Evenings in the 1980s but he replied with apologies to say that the date clashed with a television recording. However, sadly he died just months before either event. Ernie Wise, did, however, attend one of our Elstree Film Evenings in the early 1990s.

I think Morecambe & Wise will go down in history for their once eagerly awaited Christmas television spectaculars, which became the must-see event of many Christmas holidays in the 1970s. Their unique style of family entertainment endeared them to television viewers and as a result they achieved ratings that would simply be impossible to match today.'

425. What was the name of the club that was used for the filming of this episode?

426. What nickname did Eric give to the character of George Carter when he first met him in a scene?

427. What was the first name of the female impersonator Eric was seen to help change during one scene set backstage at the club – Jean, Sally or Tina?

428. Where were Professor Busby's pills hidden by the character of Wendy during part of this episode?

429. What was written on the side of the van in which Eric and Ernie escape towards the end of the episode?

430. In a car chase towards the end of the episode, what did Eric throw at the chasing cars from the back of a lorry?

Supporting Cast

There were three supporting cast members who most appeared with Morecambe & Wise on the television shows they made for the BBC – Ann Hamilton, Arthur Tolcher and Janet Webb. In this section you have the opportunity to answer 10 questions on each of them.

 Ann Hamilton

Arguably the third member of Morecambe & Wise, Ann Hamilton gave excellent support to Eric and Ernie, mainly in their BBC television shows in which she appeared in many of the sketches playing everything from a shop assistant to a member of the Salvation Army.

431. Where was Ann born?

432. In which year did Ann join the famous Windmill Theatre in London – 1958, 1959 or 1960?

433. In which year did Ann first encounter Eric and Ernie?

434. Which West End musical did Ann appear in with Bruce Forsyth?

435. Name the character which Ann played in the 'Antony and Cleopatra' sketch.

436. What role did Ann play in the sketch 'The Adventures of Robin Hood'?

437. True or false: Ann appeared in the BBC sitcom *Whatever Happened to the Likely Lads*??

438. True or false: Ann also appeared on stage with Morecambe & Wise?

439. Ann was once offered the role of the girlfriend of which character in the ITV soap *Coronation Street* – Ken Barlow, Len Fairclough or Billy Walker?

440. In which year did Ann retire from show business?

 Janet Webb

No doubt, Janet Webb – if she were alive today – would have liked to have added a postscript to this publication thanking you all for buying and reading her little book! For, as all true Morecambe & Wise fans will know, Janet often made a memorable speech at the end of Eric and Ernie's television shows thanking us for '...watching me and my little show!'.

441. Where was Janet born – Leeds, Liverpool or Manchester?

442. What was the name of the film Janet appeared in that starred Zero Mostel and Phil Silvers?

443. Complete the title of the 1970 comedy short Janet appeared in – '*It's the Only* ___ __ __'.

444. True or false: Janet did not appear with Eric and Ernie on television until they moved to the BBC?

445. What was the name of the *Dad's Army* actor whom Janet was supposedly set to marry after meeting on *The Morecambe & Wise Show*?

446. True or false: Janet appeared in *The Morecambe & Wise Christmas Show* in 1972?

447. True or false: Janet appeared with Sid James and Kenneth Connor in the one-off television sitcom special *All This and Christmas Too!*?

448. What was the title of the Frankie Howerd sitcom that Janet once made an appearance in?

449. Complete the title of the saucy film in which Janet played the role of Vera – *The _____ Milkman*.

450. How many editions of *The Morecambe & Wise Show* made for Thames Television did Janet appear in – none, five or ten?

 ## Arthur Tolcher

Who could ever forget Arthur Tolcher's desperate but sadly thwarted attempts to play the harmonica on *The Morecambe & Wise Show*? But away from Eric and Ernie's show, Arthur had many other credits in the business, including bookings where he was actually allowed to play the harmonica without being interrupted by the double act!

451. On what date was Arthur born?

452. Where was Arthur born?

453. Eric and Ernie worked with Arthur at the Swansea Empire in which year – 1938, 1939 or 1940?

454. True or false: Arthur played the harmonica on at least one record made by the singer Frank Ifield?

455. What tune did Arthur constantly try to play during *The Morecambe & Wise Show*?

456. In which year did Arthur first appear on *The Morecambe & Wise Christmas Show*?

457. True or false: Arthur appeared in certain editions of Morecambe & Wise's radio shows in the 1970s?

458. True or false: Arthur released a novelty record called
     Not Now, Arthur in 1974?

459. Which BBC radio station broadcast a documentary on Arthur
     in 2007?

460. In which year did Arthur pass away – 1987, 1988 or
     1989?

Special Guests

Here's your chance to try to answer questions on just 10 of the many special guests who appeared with Morecambe & Wise on their television shows.

 Dame Shirley Bassey

461. Where was Dame Shirley born?

462. Complete the title of the song that Dame Shirley had a number two hit with in the 1960s – 'As Long As __ _____ __'.

463. True or false: Dame Shirley is the only singer to have recorded more than one James Bond theme song?

464. How many Christmas shows made by Morecambe & Wise did Dame Shirley appear on – two, three or four?

465. In which year did Dame Shirley first appear on *The Morecambe & Wise Christmas Show*?

466. What was the title of the song that Dame Shirley sang during the famous boot sketch?

467. During the boot sketch, what happened to Dame Shirley as she reached the bottom of a small staircase?

468. When was Dame Shirley given her damehood?

469. How many years in show business did Dame Shirley celebrate in 2003?

470. True or false: Dame Shirley appeared at the Glastonbury music festival in 2006?

Peter Cushing

471. On which date was Peter born – 24 May 1913, 25 May 1913 or 26 May 1913?

472. Where was Peter born?

473. True or false: Peter once appeared in a film with Laurel and Hardy?

474. How many times did Peter play the role of Dr Who on film?

475. In which year did Peter first appear on *The Morecambe & Wise Show*?

476. What role was Peter given in one of Ernie's plays during the actor's first appearance on *The Morecambe & Wise Show*?

477. Which legendary film company, best known for its horror films, did Peter often work for?

478. What did Peter trick Eric and Ernie into finally doing when he appeared on one of their Christmas Specials for Thames Television?

479. What role did Peter play in the 1976 film *Star Wars*?

480. On which date did Peter pass away?

Did You Know?

On an edition of *The Morecambe & Wise Show* in which Dame Shirley Bassey sang 'Diamonds Are Forever', Eric walked up to Dame Shirley and, eyeing her beautiful glittering dress, said: 'You look like a Brillo pad!'

Hannah Gordon

481. Where was Hannah born?

482. True or false: Hannah appeared with Eric and Ernie on an edition of their show made for ATV?

483. Complete the title of the following film that Hannah appeared in: *Spring and _____ _____*.

484. How many Christmas shows did Hannah appear in with Morecambe & Wise?

485. What was the title of the song that Hannah sang on her first appearance with Eric and Ernie?

486. On which date did Hannah first appear in a show Morecambe & Wise made for Thames Television?

487. Which Shakespearean character did Hannah play in one of Ernie's legendary play adaptations?

488. Complete the title of a drama series Hannah appeared in – *Telford's _____*.

489. What role did Hannah play in the drama *My Family and Other Animals*?

490. In which sitcom did Hannah play the role of Belinda Braithwaite?

 Dame Glenda Jackson

491. Where was Dame Glenda born?

492. Where did Dame Glenda study to be an actress – LAMDA, Mountview or RADA?

493. In which year did Dame Glenda appear in the drama series *Elizabeth R*?

494. On which date did Dame Glenda first appear on *The Morecambe & Wise Show* – 3 June 1973, 4 June 1973 or 5 June 1973?

495. What Morecambe & Wise sketch is Dame Glenda most famous for appearing in?

496. After first appearing on *The Morecambe & Wise Show*, what film was Dame Glenda offered a role in?

497. At the end of a routine which featured Dame Glenda impersonating Ginger Rogers, what happened to the actress?

498. In which year was Dame Glenda made a CBE – 1977, 1978 or 1979?

499. True or false: Dame Glenda played Patricia Neal in the 1981 biographical television drama, *The Patricia Neal Story*?

500. In which year did Dame Glenda first become a politician?

Helen Lederer

Helen Lederer is one of Britain's best-known comedy character actresses. She says:

'I loved the sketch with Glenda Jackson – a proper Shakespearean actress having to put up with two bumbling idiots in an am-dram sketch – she gave off a gravitas that the situation didn't deserve.

Similarly, the wonderful Dame Shirley Bassey found great mileage in her solo boot acting and managed to look darn gorgeous. Maybe we should all wear one boot with a silver evening dress!'

Penelope Keith

501. Where was Penelope born?

502. True or false: Penelope's appearance in the film *Carry On Doctor* never made it on to the screen?

503. Where did Penelope first meet Eric and Ernie – ATV Centre, Borehamwood, BBC Television Centre or London Palladium?

504. What was the name of the character Penelope played in the sitcom *The Good Life*?

505. What was wrong with the staircase Penelope walked down with Eric and Ernie in their 1977 Christmas show?

506. How many editions of *The Morecambe and Christmas Show* did Penelope appear in – one, two or three?

507. Complete the title of the Thames Television sitcom Penelope appeared in with Peter Bowles – *Executive* _____.

508. True or false: Penelope played the lead role in the sitcom *No Job for a Lady*?

509. Which panel show did Penelope once present?

510. What was the title of the sitcom Penelope appeared in and which returned for a Christmas special in 2007?

 Des O'Connor

511. Where was Des born?

512. In which year did Eric first meet Des?

513. True or false: Des once toured with the legendary singer Buddy Holly?

514. On hearing that Des had asked the audience of one of his shows to pray for Eric following his first heart attack, what did Eric reportedly say?

515. In which year did Morecambe & Wise first perform an anti-Des joke on an edition of their show – 1972, 1973 or 1974?

516. True or false: Eric's wife once caught him playing one of Des's records in his study?

517. What did Eric maintain Des's first name was short for?

518. True or false: Des never did sing on *The Morecambe & Wise Show*?

519. True or false: one of Des's television shows broke the ratings record for BBC2, previously held by *The Morecambe & Wise Show*?

520. Name the Channel 4 quiz show that Des has presented in recent times?

Dave Prowse

Best known for playing the Green Cross Code man in a successful road traffic safety campaign and for climbing into the Darth Vader costume for the first trilogy of the *Star Wars* film series, Dave also worked with Eric and Ernie:

'I had the great pleasure of working with Eric and Ernie twice. First I appeared in a "Lady Chatterley's Lover" sketch and second in a "Rent a Giant – RAG" sketch. On both occasions I found Eric and Ernie hilarious, very professional and I am very proud to be able to say that we worked together – it is also great for my CV!'

André Previn

521. In which year did André appear in the 'Grieg piano concerto' sketch?

522. Off-air, where did André tell Eric and Ernie he had learnt his lines for his first appearance on their show?

523. During the 'Grieg piano concerto' sketch, where does André say he has left his baton?

524. Name two of the alternative second names that were given to André during his appearances with Morecambe & Wise.

525. In the 'Grieg piano concerto' sketch, what did André have to do so that Eric could see his cue to start playing the piano?

526. What is reportedly said to have happened at a concert, staged shortly after the first broadcast of the 'Grieg piano concerto' sketch, when André started to conduct the same piece of music?

527. True or false: André did not take part on a record release that featured a version of the 'Grieg piano concerto' sketch?

528. In which year did André appear on one of Eric and Ernie's Christmas shows made for Thames?

529. Who is André's favourite composer?

530. What is the title of André's memoirs published in 1991?

 Sir Cliff Richard

531. Where was Sir Cliff born?

532. In which year did Sir Cliff record his first single?

533. What was the name of the group that once backed Sir Cliff?

534. In which year did Sir Cliff make the film *The Young Ones*?

535. In a famous flat sketch on an edition of the double act's show that featured Sir Cliff, what kind of model was Eric seen painting?

536. When practising a song and dance routine in a flat sketch, what did Eric give Sir Cliff to use as a pretend microphone?

537. What song did Sir Cliff sing in the aforementioned flat sketch – 'Living Doll', 'Summer Holiday' or 'The Young Ones'?

538. What household object did Sir Cliff, Eric and Ernie each dance with during 'The Fleet's In' number?

539. In which year did Sir Cliff perform on a single for Comic Relief with members of the cast of the sitcom *The Young Ones* – 1984, 1985 or 1986?

540. In which year was Sir Cliff knighted?

 Dame Diana Rigg

541. Where was Dame Diana born?

542. Which action television series is Dame Diana best known for appearing in?

543. Which James Bond film did Dame Diana appear in?

544. What character did Dame Diana play in a sketch on *The Morecambe & Wise Show*?

545. At which castle did Dame Diana film exterior scenes with Eric and Ernie for the show she appeared in?

546. On what date did location filming for Dame Diana's sketch take place –17 November 1975, 18 November 1975 or 19 November 1975?

547. What message could clearly be seen on the bottom of a bed that was raised at the end of a sketch that Dame Diana appeared in?

548. True or false: Dame Diana appeared in the film *The Great Muppet Caper*?

549. Which Stephen Sondheim musical did Dame Diana appear in during 1986?

550. True or false: Dame Diana appeared in the Ricky Gervais sitcom *Extras*?

 Angela Rippon

551. In which year did Angela first read the nine o'clock news on the BBC?

552. In which year did Angela make her first appearance with Morecambe & Wise on their Christmas show – 1974, 1975 or 1976?

553. True or false: Angela sang and danced to the song '"A" You're Adorable' as part of sketch on an edition of *The Morecambe & Wise Christmas Show*?

554. Which contest did Angela host for the BBC in May 1977?

555. True or false: Angela also appeared in *The Morecambe & Wise Christmas Show* in 1978?

556. Which royal event did Angela present the BBC's coverage of in 1981?

557. What was the title of the BBC dancing show that Angela once hosted?

558. True or false: Angela occasionally read the news on *The Big Breakfast* during its run?

559. In which year was Angela awarded the OBE?

560. What was the title of the musical in which Angela toured during 2006?

Complete The Names

The list of guests, singers and musical acts who were only to pleased to appear and be insulted on *The Morecambe & Wise Show* is very long, but see just how many of the names you can complete.

 Special Guests

561. Late actor, father of Vanessa, Corin and Lynn: Michael _____.

562. Late presenter of *Mastermind*: Magnus _____.

563. Late actor whose third wife was Dame Joan Plowright: Laurence _____.

564. Actor who played T.J. Middleditch in ITV1's *The Royal*: Ian _____.

565. Puppet sidekick of the late children's favourite, Harry Corbett: _____.

566. Actress best known for appearing in the sitcom *Terry and June*: June _____.

567. Actress known for having appeared in the ferry-based soap *Triangle*:_____ O'Mara.

568. BBC TV commentator and chairman of *Question Time*: _____ Dimbleby.

569. Actor who appeared in the sitcom *To The Manor Born*: _____ Bowles.

570. Actor best known for playing the lead role in *Return of the Saint*: ____ Ogilvy.

571. Late actor best known for his stage appearances at the Old Vic: Ralph _____.

572. Actress who was once married to Dennis Waterman: Rula _____.

573. Actor who played a lead role in *All Creatures Great and Small*:_____ Hardy.

574. Veteran broadcaster and now a columnist for the *Sunday Express*: _____ Young.

575. Actor who played Harry Grout in the classic sitcom *Porridge*:_____ Vaughan.

576. Late actress who was once a Rank starlet: Diana _____.

577. Actor who appeared in the drama series *Shoestring*: Trevor ___.

578. British journalist, broadcaster and author: Ludovic _____.

579. Late American-born violinist and conductor: _____ Menuhin.

580. Well-known actor, choreographer and dancer: Wayne _____.

Singers and Musical Acts

581. Joe Brown and his _____.

582. The Mike _____ Singers.

583. The _____ Brothers.

584. Jack _____ and His Orchestra.

585. The _____ in a Crowd.

Tammy Jones

Born in north Wales, Tammy Jones began singing at a very early age. She went on to establish herself as a regular on both radio and television in her native Wales and then starred in her own TV series *Tammy*. She says:

'I have lovely memories of Morecambe & Wise. For instance, the night before we were recording their show, I was singing away at a rehearsal and I could hear Eric and Ernie whispering and joking behind me, saying that they should have brought sandwiches as they would be there all night as I was singing a slow song! There I was trying to keep a straight face and trying to sing but just wanting to laugh! Eric and Ernie were really nice to me and it was a pleasure singing on their show. I have a copy of that show and, would you believe, it has been shown here twice in New Zealand, where I now live. It was very exciting to see the show again after all these years.'

586. The _____ Sisters.

587. Humphrey _____ and His Band.

588. The Dave _____ Five.

589. The ___ Faces.

590. Freddie and the _____.

591. The Mike _____ Jazzmen.

592. Herman's _____.

593. Matt _____.

594. Tom _____.

595. The Fraser Hayes _____.

COMPLETE THE NAMES

596. Vince _____.
597. Sasha _____.
598. Nana _____.
599. Kiki ____.
600. Frankie _____.

Production Team

The Morecambe & Wise Show was blessed with excellent writers, producers, directors, choreographers and other contributors. In this section you can test your knowledge of just a few of the many people who worked behind the scenes on Morecambe & Wise's show.

 Johnny Ammonds

Johnny Ammonds worked as a producer and director on several editions of *The Morecambe & Wise Show* at both the BBC and at Thames Television.

601. What position did Johnny first obtain when he joined the BBC?

602. Complete the title of the television show Johnny produced in the 1960s – *Lulu's Back __ _____*.

603. Complete the name of the book which Johnny wrote the foreword for – *My Name is Harry _____*.

604. What is the name of the Irish singer whose shows Johnny once produced?

605. In which year was Johnny awarded the MBE?

606. Which film inspired Johnny to adapt a dance for Eric and Ernie that was originally performed by Groucho Marx?

607. True or false: Johnny produced and directed 'The Stripper' sketch?

608. How many series of *The Morecambe & Wise Show* did Johnny produce and direct for Eric and Ernie at Thames – two, three or four?

609. True or false: Johnny worked on Eric and Ernie's 1982 Christmas special?

610. Complete the title of the 2002 documentary on British TV light entertainment in which Johnny appeared – *The Showbiz ___.*

 Eddie Braben

Eddie Braben was the award-winning writer who wrote many of Morecambe & Wise's radio and television shows.

611. Where was Eddie born?

612. In which year did Eddie become a professional comedy writer?

613. Which well-known comedian did Eddie sell his first-ever joke to – Charlie Chester, Benny Hill or Jimmy Tarbuck?

614. True or false: Eddie once wrote material for Peter Sellers?

615. At which theatre did the Morecambe & Wise writer Eddie first see Eric and Ernie appear?

616. Name the American singer who was on the same bill the first time Eddie saw Eric and Ernie perform.

617. In which year did Eddie receive a BAFTA award for 'outstanding contribution to television'?

618. How many years did Eddie write for Morecambe & Wise – 12, 13 or 14?

619. Eric, Ernie and Eddie came to be known as what in the TV industry?

620. What mutual hobby did Eric and Eddie share?

Tony Hatch

Tony Hatch was one of the leading composers of popular songs and music for television. Here, Tony recalls how positive thinking helped Morecambe & Wise, and, in turn, himself:

'I wrote the song "Positive Thinking" *specifically* for Morecambe & Wise (my former wife, Jackie Trent, co-wrote the lyrics). The year was 1971. Eric and Ernie personally asked for something bright and cheerful that could work as an alternative to their usual "Bring Me Sunshine" in their TV shows. They also included "Positive Thinking" in their stage shows.

I knew Eric and Ernie quite well. Jackie had appeared on their TV show and was sometimes the female singing guest in their stage shows. I also met them frequently at Variety Club charity events.

"Positive Thinking" was my idea for the title. There had been a best-selling book in 1952 called *The Power of Positive Thinking* written by the so-called "father of positive thinking", Norman Vincent Peale. Even in the 1970s the phrase "positive thinking" was still in regular use.

I did a quick demo and Eric and Ernie liked it immediately. A songwriter can't ask for more. Their huge viewing figures made the song instantly popular and they adopted it as their own. They also "adapted" it because, in fact, the melody they sing isn't quite "the tune what I wrote". Who cares? They made it famous and the words "positive thinking" are now more identified with Morecambe & Wise than Norman Vincent Peale.

Many years ago we went to Biagi's Restaurant in Upper Berkeley Street, London W1. Eric, with two or three others, was halfway through his meal at a nearby table. By then he

and Ernie were regularly performing "Positive Thinking".
Shortly after we received the menu Eric crawled on all fours
over to our table and shouted in my ear, "HERE'S SOME
POSITIVE THINKING – DON'T HAVE THE FISH!"
He then crawled back again to his own table. Being a small
restaurant, nobody could miss seeing or hearing him. Only
Eric Morecambe could do such a thing and not be asked to
leave on account of disorderly conduct.

Jackie and I also had the pleasure of entertaining Ernie
and his wife Doreen on our boat in Sydney when he toured
Australia with his one-man show following Eric's untimely
death. (Actually, it was really a two-man show because Ernie
"wisely" included many hilarious Eric and Ernie TV clips.)

 ## Bill Cotton

Bill Cotton was once the head of variety at the BBC and responsible for bringing Morecambe & Wise back to the company after they left ATV.

621. In which year was Bill born – 1927, 1928 or 1929?

622. Name the television series which Bill's late father once had on the BBC.

623. True or false: Bill was once a producer on the music show *Six-Five Special*?

624. In which year did Bill become the head of variety at BBC television?

625. When Morecambe & Wise moved to Thames, how did Bill describe the situation?

626. In which year did Bill become controller of BBC1?

627. In which year did Bill receive a BAFTA Academy Fellowship award?

628. In which year was Bill the subject of the television programme *This is Your Life*?

629. In which year was Bill made a CBE?

630. In which year did Bill appear in the TV documentary series *The Story of Light Entertainment*?

 Mike Craig

Mike Craig wrote additional material for Morecambe & Wise.

631. Where was Mike born?

632. At which of the following theatres did Mike first experience live entertainment – Dewsbury Empire, Hackney Empire or Sunderland Empire?

633. In which year did Mike begin writing seriously?

634. Roughly how many television and radio programmes had Mike worked on during his long career – 1,000, 1,100 or 1,200?

635. As well as a writer, what position did Mike once hold at the BBC?

636. True or false: Mike contributed material for *The Morecambe & Wise Christmas Show* in 1976?

637. How many volumes called *Look Back with Laughter* has Mike written – four, five or six?

638. True or false: Mike used to perform a show on board cruise ships entitled *Mike Craig's ABC of Comedy*?

639. What was the title of Mike's play about Robb Wilton?

640. Complete the title of a radio show Mike once presented –
Mike Craig on the _____.

 Barry Cryer

Together with John Junkin, Barry Cryer wrote material for Morecambe & Wise.

641. Where was Barry born?

642. True or false: Barry once wrote material for the legendary comedian Bob Hope?

643. From which year onwards did Barry contribute material for *The Morecambe & Wise Show*?

644. What is the title of the BBC Radio 4 series that started in 1972 and on which Barry is a panellist?

645. Which ITV panel show did Barry once host?

646. True or false: Barry co-wrote the 1978 edition of *The Morecambe & Wise Christmas Show*?

647. True or false: Barry also wrote material for *The Two Ronnies*?

648. Name the zany radio DJ (now deceased) whose television shows Barry co-wrote for Thames Television and the BBC.

649. Name the writer with whom Barry co-wrote the Eric Morecambe tribute show *Bring Me Sunshine*.

650. In which year was Barry awarded the OBE?

Lord Lew Grade

Lord Lew Grade was responsible for giving Morecambe & Wise their first television series on ITV.

651. True or false: Lord Lew's real name was Louis Winogradsky?

652. In which year was Lord Lew born – 1906, 1907 or 1908?

653. In which year did Lord Lew become a professional dancer?

654. Name the company that Lord Lew started which made drama series and later film productions.

655. True or false: Lord Lew originally turned down the opportunity to give Morecambe & Wise a television series at ATV?

656. True or false: Lord Lew was knighted in 1967?

657. What were the names of Lord Lew's two brothers?

658. In which year was Lord Lew made a life peer – 1975, 1976 or 1977?

659. What are the names of the much-loved children's puppets that Lord Lew brought to both the small and big screen?

660. What was the title of Lord Lew's autobiography?

 Sid Green and Dick Hills

Sid Green and Dick Hills were a writing partnership who wrote for Morecambe & Wise.

661. In which year was Sid born – 1927, 1928 or 1929?

662. On what date was Dick born – 17 January 1926, 18 January 1926 or 19 January 1926?

663. In which year did Sid and Dick first write for Morecambe & Wise?

664. True or false: Sid and Dick made cameo appearances in the film *The Intelligence Men*, which starred Morecambe & Wise?

665. What was the title of Sid and Dick's own 1967 television series?

666. True or false: Sid and Dick wrote for the performer Anthony Newley?

667. Name the *Up Pompeii!* star for whom Sid and Dick wrote material.

668. In which year did Sid and Dick provide material for Morecambe & Wise while the double act were making shows at Thames Television?

669. In which year did Sid pass away?

670. On which date did Dick pass away – 6 June 1996, 7 June 1996 or 8 June 1996?

 Philip Jones

Philip Jones was once the head of light entertainment at Thames Television and responsible for helping to bring Morecambe & Wise over to the company.

671. In which year was Philip born?

672. At which radio station did Philip meet his future wife, Florence?

673. In which year did Philip join Granada as a light entertainment producer?

674. What was the name of the show Philip created that gained The Beatles their first national television exposure?

675. In which year did Philip join the television company ABC – 1960, 1961 or 1962?

676. In which year did Philip receive an OBE?

677. True or false: Bryan Cowgill helped Philip to mastermind Morecambe & Wise's transfer to Thames.

678. In which year did Philip give Michael Barrymore his first TV series – 1982, 1983 or 1984?

679. True or false: Philip worked as an executive producer on the sitcom *As Times Goes By*?

680. In which year did Philip pass away – 2002, 2003 or 2004?

 John Junkin

Together with Barry Cryer, John Junkin wrote material for Morecambe & Wise.

681. On what date was John born – 27 January 1930, 28 January 1930 or 29 January 1930?

682. True or false: John was born in Ealing, Middlesex?

683. Name the legendary comedian who starred in the film *The Rebel* and who John at one time played a foil to.

684. True or false: John appeared in The Beatles' film *A Hard Day's Night*?

685. What was the name of John's own TV series which he appeared in for Southern Television?

686. What role did John play in the sitcom *Till Death Us Do Part*?

687. Complete the title of a cult radio show John once had – *Hello* _____.

688. What role did John play in the BBC soap *EastEnders*?

689. What was the title of John Culshaw's television show for which John wrote material?

690. In which year did John pass away?

Did You Know?

One-time producer, director and choreographer of *The Morecambe & Wise Show*, Ernest Maxin, once became the victim of a practical joke set up by Eric and Ernie. Arriving home from location filming on *The Morecambe & Wise Show*, Ernest discovered that he had a black ink ring around one of his eyes after the duo had added black ink to the eyepiece on the camera. As a result, Maxin recalled getting some very strange looks while he was travelling home on a tube train in London.

 Ernest Maxin

Ernest Maxin worked as a producer, director and choreographer on certain editions of Morecambe & Wise's television shows at the BBC.

691. Where in London was Ernest born?

692. Complete the title of three specials that Ernest produced at the BBC in 1956 – *The _____ Wisdom Show*.

693. True or false: Ernest produced five editions of *The Ted Ray Show*?

694. What was the name of the Irish comedian whose BBC television shows Ernest produced in both 1968 and 1969?

695. At which of the following seaside resorts did Ernest first meet Eric and Ernie – Blackpool, Torquay or Weymouth?

696. In which year, following the duo's return to the BBC, did Ernest begin choreographing routines on *The Morecambe & Wise Show* – 1968, 1969 or 1970?

697. True or false: Ernest worked on the 'Singin' in the Rain' routine?

698. How many editions of *The Les Dawson Show* did Ernest produce for BBC television – 13, 14 or 15?

699. In which year did Ernest produce *The Mike Reid Show*?

700. True or false: Ernest worked on certain routines for Morecambe & Wise when they were at Thames?

Pot Luck 2

Now see how many of this second set of 20 pot-luck questions, all related to Morecambe & Wise, you can answer correctly.

701. Which entertainer was once quoted as saying 'It was an honour to go on a *Morecambe & Wise Show* and be insulted'?

702. True or false: Eric enjoyed flying?

703. What was Eric's favourite kind of cigar?

704. What shoe size did Eric take – six, seven or eight?

705. True or false: Eric's wife, Joan, was a former beauty queen?

706. In which year did Eric suffer his second heart attack – 1978, 1979 or 1980?

707. Which actress played the girl in the record version of a sketch 'The Ton Up Boy'?

708. In the record version of a sketch entitled 'Tape Recorder' who do we discover Eric has supposedly been having a fling with – Ernie's cousin, Ernie's sister or Ernie's wife?

709. True or false: in the record version of a sketch entitled 'Get It Right Corporal' Ernie played the corporal?

710. In which year did Eric and Ernie appear in Graham Stark's short film *Simon, Simon*?

711. Who did Eric dedicate his first novel to?

712. True or false: Eric used to keep a tape of Frank Zappa's music in his Rolls-Royce?

713. Which legendary singer and pianist did Eric and his wife Joan once take afternoon tea with at his home in Las Vegas?

714. In which year did the actor Alan Curtis, whom Morecambe & Wise worked with, recall first meeting Eric and Ernie – 1953, 1954 or 1955?

715. Which charitable trust benefited from a donation from the sales of the book *Memories of Eric*?

716. True or false: Eddie Braben, a one-time writer of *The Morecambe & Wise Show*, appeared in certain sketches on the show?

717. In which Hertfordshire venue is The Eric Morecambe Hall situated?

718. True or false: Eric was a one-time president of an amateur dramatics group called the Kimpton Players?

719. What was the name of the sketch in which Eric and Ernie parodied the drama *The Naked City*?

720. True or false: a running joke at the end of several editions of Morecambe & Wise's ATV shows included the use of various doors?

Film

Though they never quite made it to Hollywood, Eric and Ernie did make brief ventures into the world of film. This section features 40 questions on each of the films which Morecambe & Wise originally made for the cinema or television.

 The Intelligence Men

721. True or false: no second name is given for Eric's character in the film?

722. What was the name of Ernie's character in the film?

723. What was the longer title of the film when it was released in Britain?

724. Which company made the film?

725. At which famous British film studios was the film made – Ealing Studios, Pinewood Studios or Shepperton Studios?

726. In which year was the film originally released?

727. True or false: the film's running time is 120 minutes?

728. In which northern city was the film premiered?

729. What was the title of the film when it was released in America?

730. Who was the director of the film?

731. Who acted as the director of photography on the film?

732. Who composed the original music for the film?

733. What was the name of the choreographer who worked on the film?

734. Who was the writer on whose story the screenplay was based?

735. Which famous London landmark is seen briefly not long after the film begins?

736. What is the name of the major who is found dead at the start of the film?

737. What is the name of the French city in which the major is found dead?

738. Which actor, who went on to appear in *The Benny Hill Show*, played the non-speaking role of a policeman in the film – Henry McGee, Nicholas Parsons or Bob Todd?

739. Which role did actor William Franklyn play in the film?

740. Which actor, who later played one of the main roles in the TV detective series *Bergerac*, appeared in the film?

741. True or false: the actor David Lodge appeared in the film?

742. What piece of office furniture were Eric and Ernie seen to perform a dance routine on during the early part of the film?

743. Who was the ballerina Eric and Ernie's characters were trying to protect in the film?

744. True or false: Charles Hawtrey, best-known for appearing in the *Carry On* Films, played a doctor in this film?

745. What was the name of the actor who went on to play Mike Baldwin in the soap *Coronation Street* who appeared in the film?

746. Name the *Till Death Do Us Part* actor who appeared in the film.

747. What is the name of the fictitious London hotel featured in the film?

748. True or false: the woman featured in a scene in a lift in the film was played by actress Marianne Stone?

749. What was the name of the transport café which Eric and Ernie arrived at on motorbikes during the film?

750. What happened when Eric tried to park his motorbike at the transport café?

751. What was the name of the cinema that Eric went to in the film?

752. What time was the screening of the film Eric went to see?

753. What row and seat number did Eric have – Row E Seat 4, Row E Seat 5 or Row E Seat 6?

754. What disguise did Ernie put on in order to go undercover at the cinema?

755. What happened to Eric when he finally took his seat in the cinema?

756. What happened to the man who took Eric's seat while he went to buy an ice lolly – he was mugged, he was kissed by a woman sitting next to him or he was stabbed?

757. What was the name of the ballet that was featured in the film?

758. At which London venue was the ballet in the film supposedly staged?

759. Whereabouts in her dressing room did the Russian ballerina find a death threat?

760. While dressed as Egyptians, what happened to Eric and Ernie at the theatre during the film?

Vicki Michelle

Versatile actress Vicki Michelle is probably best known for playing the role of the saucy waitress, Yvette, in the hit BBC sitcom *'Allo 'Allo!* She says:

'Eric and Ernie were quite simply two of the most brilliant comedy performers of all time and the perfect foils for each other, a team in every sense. To me they were the epitome of situation comedy because it didn't matter what situation you put them in, they would work their touch of genius and make it funny. I also used to marvel at the lengths they could get their guest stars to go to on their shows, particularly Glenda Jackson and Shirley Bassey.

I never worked with them, although I often used to bump into them in the infamous BBC canteen or rehearsal rooms during my early days at the BBC. The first time I met Ernie properly was at a charity event. He was so gentle and down to earth. In more recent years I have had contact with Joan Morecambe at fund-raising events given by such organisations as The Lady Taverners and Lady Ratlings. I am also fortunate to know Ernest Maxin through my connection with The Heritage Foundation. He was their producer at the Beeb from the mid 1970s and masterminded "The Boys'" tremendous success from behind the scenes.

As for a favourite sketch, where do you start? Actually, I loved the opening café scene from the film *The Intelligence Men*. Picture Eric trying to serve coffee, catch the gist of a major espionage plot, wrestle with the pronunciation of the Russian enemy spy department, memorise a theme from a well-known ballet and get Ernie to pay for his tea all at the same time! It still has me falling about. And who could forget the trademark slap Eric inflicted on Little Ern. I often wondered if it hurt so I tried it on my husband. He confirmed it does!!

Yes they brought sunshine, yes they brought laughter. In fact, they made you laugh out loud, not just smile or giggle, and they still do with their legacy today; but more than that, they brought families together to share in it. Quite an epitaph.'

That Riviera Touch

761. What was the name of Eric's character in the film?

762. What was the name of Ernie's character in the film?

763. Which actor played the role of Le Pirate in the film?

764. Who was the director of the film?

765. Who was the producer of the film?

766. Who composed the original music for the film?

767. In which year was the film released?

768. What job did Eric and Ernie's characters have at the very start of the film?

769. The exterior of which well-known royal residence in London was seen at the start of the film?

770. What inspired Eric and Ernie to choose the south of France as their holiday destination in the film?

771. Which airline did the duo travel to France with?

772. At which airport in France did Eric and Ernie land?

773. True or false: Eric and Ernie's car was the second car to be offloaded from the plane?

774. What was the first thing Eric and Eric did after they collected their car at the airport in France?

775. Over which eye did the character of Le Pirate wear an eyepatch?

776. Where did the character of Claudette make her visits to see Le Pirate?

777. Where did the character of Coco live?

778. True or false: the actress Alexandra Bastedo appeared in the film?

779. What was the name of the villa that Eric and Ernie stayed at?

780. Why were the double act persuaded to stay at the villa instead of their hotel?

781. How were the bodies at the villa dispensed with?

782. What happened to Eric when he was playing a ball game on the beach?

783. Whereabouts in Eric and Ernie's car did Le Pirate decide to hide the emeralds?

784. When handed a gambling chip at the casino in the film, what did Eric first try to do with it – eat it, throw it away or wear it?

785. In the correct order, what were the numbers which won Eric his cash at the casino – 25, 9 & 0, 26, 10 & 0 or 27, 11 & 0?

786. At which hotel did Ernie have dinner with Claudette?

787. How much did Ernie's dinner with Claudette cost – 220 francs, 230 francs or 240 francs?

788. What type of food did Ernie hide in a wine bottle holder during dinner?

789. After being kissed by Claudette on the balcony of her hotel room, what happened to Eric?

790. Where did Eric keep his winnings from the casino?

791. What was the main purchase Eric decided to make with his casino winnings?

792. How did Claudette entice Eric to wade further into the sea?

793. What happened to Eric when he started to wade into the sea?

794. While in the sea, what did someone replace Eric's money with?

795. How did Eric and Ernie blast their way out of a shed they had been locked in by the jewel thieves?

796. Where did Eric's character hire a diving suit from during the film?

797. To make their car faster, what did Eric ask Ernie to do?

798. What happened to Coco towards the end of the film?

799. What did Ernie manage do to the duo's car towards the end of the film?

800. Which of the duo's characters supposedly married Claudette at the end of the film, Eric's or Ernie's?

Did You Know?

While on location for the film *That Riviera Touch*, Eric, Ernie and their respective wives socialised with the film actors Tony Curtis and Omar Sharif, who were also filming in the south of France at the time.

 The Magnificent Two

801. What did Eric and Ernie's characters sell for a living in the film?

802. In which year was the film originally released?

803. On what date in the month of July was the film given its London premiere – 4th, 5th or 6th?

804. What is the running time of the film?

805. Who wrote the story on which the screenplay of the film was based?

806. Who was the assistant director on the film?

807. Who was the cinematographer on the film?

808. What was the name of the film when it was released in America?

809. What role did the actress Margit Saad play in the film?

810. Which actor played the British ambassador in the film?

811. Which actor played the real Torres in the film?

812. True or false: Sandor Elès, who played Armandez in the film, was later to play the role of Paul Ross in the television soap *Crossroads*?

813. What role did actor Victor Maddern play in the film – a drunken soldier, prison officer or shopkeeper?

Harry Fielder

Harry Fielder worked as a supporting artist on a large number of British film and television productions. Harry, known as 'Aitch' to his friends, recalls the two occasions on which he was lucky enough to work with the legendary comedy duo:

'The first time I worked with Morecambe & Wise was on their third film, which was called *The Magnificent Two*. Both Eric and Ernie made us all feel very welcome and the days working on the film were really fun.

In the early 1980s I met up with the double act again when we were all working on a children's programme made by Thames Television called *CBTV*. We had a really great day working on the programme and they were just as nice. They'll always stay in my memory.'

814. Which actress played Juanita in the film?

815. True or false: President Diaz was played by actor Jon Pertwee?

816. Which role did actor Larry Taylor play in the film?

817. The actor son of *Carry On* star Peter Butterworth appeared in this film. What is his name?

818. Which James Bond film was being filmed at the same studios when the film was being made?

819. Which park situated close to Pinewood Studios was used for certain location work on the film – Black Park, Green Park or Pinetree Park?

820. What was the name of the then James Bond actor who visited Eric and Ernie on the set of the film?

821. True or false: the film company responsible for the special effects on the film was Bowie Films?

822. At the start of the film, what prevented Eric's character from leaving the train carriage the proper way?

823. What happened to the real Torres at the very start of the film?

824. What did Ernie say he wanted to do once they left the station?

825. Where did Eric and Ernie hide in the film during a shoot-out that started shortly after they arrived by train at the start of this film?

826. How much money did Eric accept to impersonate the recently killed rebel leader Torres – one million pesos, two million pesos or three million pesos?

827. How many daughters did President Diaz have in the film – one, two or three?

828. What was so appealing to Eric and Ernie about the washing facilities at the revolutionaries' camp?

829. How did the character of Juanita foresee Eric's death during the film?

830. When posing as a president in the film, how many medals did Eric have on his jacket – two, three or four?

831. At a banquet held in Eric's honour, what did the British ambassador suggest to him that he could become?

832. During a television broadcast, what did Eric do when his autocue failed?

833. When Eric and Ernie helped to rescue President Diaz's children towards the end of the film, what type of vehicle did they use?

Did You Know?
The provisional title of a 1980 film Morecambe & Wise were originally meant to have made was *Do it Yourself*.

834. What type of museum did Eric and Ernie get taken to by President Diaz's children towards the end of the film?

835. What did Eric and Ernie use to make it appear that there were more soldiers on guard at the museum?

836. What did Carillo do to Eric and Ernie when he discovered them at the museum?

837. When believing they were about to die, what did Eric ask Ernie to forgive him for doing when they used to play cards?

838. How did the female revolutionaries distract Carillo's soldiers at the museum?

839. At the very end of the film, what did Eric and Ernie both decide to do?

840. True or false: Eric and Ernie were both seen wearing red dresses at the very end of the film?

 Night Train to Murder

841. Who was the director of the film?

842. What were the names of the three people who wrote the screenplay for the film?

843. What were the names of the two people whose idea the film was based on?

844. Who was the executive producer of the film?

845. True or false: the film was not broadcast until after Eric's death?

846. On what date was the film first broadcast on ITV?

847. Which of the following people was in charge of casting the film – Marcia Stanton, Shirley Teece or Dale White?

848. Which actor, who played a prison officer in the classic sitcom *Porridge*, also appeared in the film?

849. Which actress, who played Angie in the sitcom *Three Up, Two Down*, played Eric's niece, Kathy, in the film?

850. Which actress played cousin Zelda in the film?

851. True or false: the actress who played cousin Zelda later appeared in the Thames Television sitcom *French Fields*?

852. Actor Richard Vernon played which character in the film?

853. True or false: this film was made by LWT?

854. In which year was the film set – 1944, 1945 or 1946?

855. What did Eric and Ernie's characters do for a living in the film – comedy double act, jugglers or magicians?

856. Who was the one-time *Hi-de-Hi!* actor who played the role of the theatre manager in the film – Ben Aris, Jeffrey Holland or Paul Shane?

857. Which actor played the roles of both a butler and chief superintendent in the film?

858. Which actor played a knife-thrower in the film?

859. Which character did actress Margaret Courtenay play in this film?

860. Where was the first scene in the film set?

861. In which Cumbrian city was the theatre seen at the start of this film supposedly situated?

862. On the theatre poster seen in the foyer of the theatre at the start of the film, what was the week-commencing date for the show Eric and Ernie were appearing in – Monday 22 September, Monday 23 September or Monday 24 September?

863. What were the twice-nightly performance times for the show Morecambe & Wise were supposedly appearing in?

864. What was the name of the revue Eric and Ernie were said to be appearing in?

865. What was the name of the theatre the duo were appearing at when they are first discovered at the start of the film – Empire Theatre, Her Majesty's Theatre or Theatre Royal?

866. Who was advertised as supposedly appearing at the theatre the following week after Morecambe & Wise – Max Bygraves, Des O'Connor or Cliff Richard?

Norman Lovett

Best known for playing Holly, the ship's computer in the hit BBC sitcom *Red Dwarf*, Norman Lovett shares his thoughts on Morecambe & Wise, and a special room at The Roses Theatre, Tewkesbury – the last venue Eric ever performed at:

'I was a huge fan of Eric Morecambe; he was so relaxed and funny. I recall that there was once a sketch on *The Morecambe & Wise Show* which featured Elton John at Watford football ground and it was really funny. I can't remember exactly how it went, but I know Elton John was dressed like Eric with a cap and pipe. For me, Ernie was the perfect straight man and of course that made the double act perfect because, apart from Laurel and Hardy, no double act got even close to them as far as I was concerned.

I appeared at The Roses Theatre in Tewkesbury in the early part of 2008 and I was in the Eric Morecambe Green Room before the show started, and it was impossible not to keep thinking of Eric throughout the evening.'

867. True or false: Eric's character wore a neck brace for part of the film?

868. What was the name of the hall that Eric and Ernie travel to in Scotland?

869. What was the registration of the taxi that took Eric and Ernie to the station in a scene in the film – GBH 286, GBH 287 or GBH 288?

870. True or false: it started to rain at the station while Eric and Ernie were trying to board the train?

871. What game did Eric, Ernie and the solicitor play during part of the train journey in the film?

872. When demonstrating their new mime act, what was the name of the song the duo played on a gramophone player?

873. True or false: Eric's character wore a rather obvious wig during part of the film?

874. What was the name of the book that Ernie was reading at various times in the film?

875. In a scene in which the double act were both reading in bed, what was the title of the magazine Eric was reading?

876. What happened to Eric and Ernie's bed while staying at the hall?

877. What was the telephone number of the police that the chief superintendent gives to Eric and Ernie towards the end of the film – Whitehall 1-2 1-2, Whitehall 2-1 2-1 or Whitehall 2-2 2-2?

878. True or false: the film was originally intended to also be shown in cinemas?

879. What was the name of the song that Eric and Ernie sang an extract from at the very end of the film?

880. In which year did the company Prism Leisure first release this title on DVD – 2002, 2003 or 2004?

Records

Many records were released that featured a selection of Morecambe & Wise's highly popular sketches and/or songs. In this section, why not try to see how many of the following 20 song or sketch titles you can complete?

881. 'Not Now _____'.
882. 'Me and My _____'.
883. 'Singing the _____'.
884. 'Battery _____'.
885. 'Byron and _____'.
886. 'Bath Time for _____'.
887. 'The Ambassador of _____'.
888. 'Ern, You've Got a Magnificent _____'.
889. 'The Diamond Ring in the _____'.
890. 'Carry On ___'.
891. 'Just Around the _____ '.
892. 'The _____ Bla'.
893. 'We're ___ ____'.
894. 'Songs of _____'.
895. 'Now That _____ ____'.
896. 'The ___ Side'.
897. 'Why Did I ___ ___ __'.
898. '(We Get Along So Easily) _____ ___ _____?'.
899. 'Bingle _____'.
900. 'The _____ _____ of All'.

Catchphrases

As we all know, Eric Morecambe and Ernie Wise had several memorable catchphrases. See how many of the following 10 catchphrases you can complete.

901. 'You can't see the _____'.
902. 'This boy's a _____'.
903. 'Be _____'.
904. 'Now there's a _____'.
905. 'Get out __ _____'.
906. 'What do you _____ __ __ __ ___?'.
907. 'Look at me _____ _ __ _____ __ ___'.
908. 'I don't go _____ _____'.
909. 'He's _____ _ _____'.
910. 'Get ___'.

Books

When it comes to books, Morecambe & Wise have inspired many, many titles over the years. From albums to biographies, fans of the late double act have had a huge choice of excellent publications to choose from. See how many of the following 20 questions connected with books relating to Eric Morecambe and/or Ernie Wise you can complete.

911. Complete the title of Gary Morecambe's 2003 book: *Eric Morecambe – Life's Not Hollywood it's* _____.

912. Which footballer appeared in a photo story in the book *The Morecambe & Wise Special*?

913. Which book about the late film star Will Hay did Eric write the foreword for?

914. Complete the following book title: *The Best of Morecambe & Wise:* _ _____.

915. What was the title of the football quiz book that Eric wrote the foreword for?

916. In which year was Michael Parkinson's book, which included his interview with Eric and Ernie, first published?

917. What was the title of Michael Freedland's 1981 book on Morecambe & Wise?

918. What was the title of the book that Ernie supervised the publishing of while Eric was recovering from his first heart attack?

919. What was the name of the writer who 'refereed' Morecambe & Wise's 1973 autobiography?

920. Complete the title of a photo story printed in *The Morecambe & Wise Special*: 'Last Tango in _____'.

921. What was the title of the book that William Cook edited and which featured Eric Morecambe as its subject?

922. Complete the title of Eddie Braben's book: *The Book What I Wrote: _____ _____ ___ __*.

923. Who wrote the foreword for the book *Morecambe & Wise – Behind the Sunshine*?

924. Who were the two authors of the 1994 book *Bring Me Laughter*?

925. True or false: Eric's widow, Joan, wrote the foreword for the book *Memories of Eric*?

926. In which year was *The Illustrated Eric Morecambe* first published – 1986, 1987 or 1988?

927. In which year was *The Morecambe & Wise Family Fun Book* first published?

928. Complete the title of: *Bring Me Sunshine: A _____ of Morecambe & Wise*.

929. True or false: Robert Ross wrote a 1999 book entitled *Ernie Wise: A Biography*?

930. How many pages are there in the book *Morecambe & Wise – Behind the Sunshine* – 260, 261 or 262?

Did You Know?

Eric had started a third children's novel entitled *The Vampire King*, which his son, Gary, was to finish after his death.

Luton Town FC

Any viewer who has ever seen a re-run of an edition of *The Morecambe & Wise Show* over the years will be aware of Eric's passion for Luton Town FC, due to the constant references he made to the team. But just how much do you know about exactly how Eric was involved with Luton Town and about the history of the football club itself? The following 10 questions will test your knowledge.

931. In which year was Luton Town FC formed?

932. In which year did the club turn professional?

933. In a diary entry made on Saturday 25 January 1969, how many goals did Eric say Luton had beaten Walsall by – one, two or three?

934. On which date did Eric first become a director of Luton Town FC – 30 January 1970, 31 January 1970 or 1 February 1970?

935. On which date did Eric resign from his post as director of Luton Town FC – 1974, 1975 or 1976?

936. True or false: Eric was later made a vice president of the club?

937. What did Eric say he thought Luton players looked like when they wore white shirts and black shorts?

938. What is the full title of the function room named after Eric at Luton Town FC?

939. What did Eric use a Luton Town FC rosette to cover in a sketch with the actor Peter Barkworth?

940. At a football match held at Luton's home ground shortly after Eric's death, what did the fans chant as a mark of respect?

Roger Wash

Roger Wash is Luton Town FC's official club historian. Below, Roger recalls his memories of Eric's famous association with the football club:

'Eric started to watch Luton in the late 1960s in an attempt to indoctrinate son Gary to the game. The Luton secretary at the time made sure that Eric's seat was next to the directors' box, which led to him being asked to the boardroom for drinks after each game. This, in turn, led to him becoming a director of the club.

With *The Morecambe & Wise Shows* playing to huge audiences and the "Hatters" doing well on the pitch, it was a marriage made in heaven. Eric mentioning his beloved football team at every opportunity was the best PR a club could wish for.

Although Eric took his director role at the club very seriously, he obviously loved an audience and played up to the cameras at every opportunity. In those days the club used to charter special trains to away games for the princely sum of 25s/- (£1.25). And wherever we went, the players and officials took up a couple of carriages as well. My abiding memory is of Eric walking up and down the corridors chatting to the supporters, practising his paper bag trick, adjusting people's glasses and generally acting the fool for hours on end.

A genuinely nice man and a natural comedian as well.'

Bring Me Sunshine Tribute Show

Following Eric Morecambe's death, ITV televised a stage tribute to the much-missed comedian entitled *Bring Me Sunshine*. In this section you will find 20 questions relating to this special show.

941. At which West End theatre was this show staged?

942. Which television company made this show?

943. On what date was this show staged – 7 November 1984, 8 November 1984 or 9 November 1984?

944. On which date was the television version shown on ITV?

945. How long was the running time of the television version?

946. For which charity did this special show raise funds?

947. Which member of the royal family was the guest of honour at the stage performance?

948. Who hosted this show – Bruce Forsyth, Jimmy Tarbuck or Ernie Wise?

949. What was the name of the comedian whose appearance on this show marked his return to the stage after an absence of 25 years?

950. True or false: Roy Castle choreographed this show?

951. Who acted as a consultant for the makers of this show?

952. What was the name of the director of this production?

953. Who were the executive producers on this show?

954. How many pages did the souvenir brochure for this show contain – 72, 73 or 74?

955. What was the name of the comedy double act, whose theme tune was 'Everything Will Be Okay', who appeared in this show?

956. Which comedian, who later hosted the game show *Big Break*, appeared in this special show?

957. True or false: the Tiller Girls appeared in this show?

958. What was the name of the one-time *Price is Right* host who appeared in this show?

959. What was the name of the wife of actor, author and filmmaker Bryan Forbes who appeared in this show?

960. True or false: Peter Le Page worked as the designer on this show?

Susie Pierce

The Roses Theatre is a live and film performance venue in Tewkesbury, Gloucestershire. Eric Morecambe collapsed there shortly after leaving the stage and passed away hours later. Theatre press officer Susie Pierce shares a little about the venue's special Eric Morecambe Room:

'The Eric Morecambe Room is dedicated to the memory of Eric Morecambe and his last performance at The Roses Theatre, Tewkesbury. This room has a wonderful air of peace and tranquillity and perfectly catches the rays of the afternoon sunshine. Currently used as a meeting room and to host small private events, The Eric Morecambe Room is also used as a green room prior to performances in the bar area and during the pantomime season.'

The Eric Morecambe Statue

A fine and lasting tribute created to remind the world of Eric's genius has taken the form of a statue. In this section you will find 10 questions about the statue.

961. In which northern seaside town is the statue situated?

962. Which sculptor created the statue?

963. How long did it take the sculptor to make the statue – five, six or seven years?

964. Which member of the royal family unveiled the statue?

965. On which date was the statue unveiled – 22 July 1999, 23 July 1999 or 24 July 1999?

966. How many celebrity names are displayed near the statue – 101, 102 or 103?

967. True or false: the statue's front faces the sea?

968. Which song was played as the statue was unveiled?

969. What object is Eric wearing around his neck on his statue?

970. True or false: when Eric was a boy both he and his father used to go fishing close to where the statue is now situated?

The Play What I Wrote

Proving successful wherever it is staged, *The Play What I Wrote* is a show which pays tribute to the genius of Morecambe & Wise. Below you will find 10 questions relating to this award-winning show, which has helped to bring the essence of the late double act back to the stage.

971. Who were the two main performers who appeared in the show?

972. On what date did the show first debut – 25 September 2001, 26 September 2001 or 27 September 2001?

973. At which theatre did the play first make its debut?

974. What was the name of the well-known actor and film director who directed the show?

975. What was the name of the one-time *Brookside* actor, who played a character known as 'Sinbad', who appeared as the first celebrity guest in the show?

976. True or false: Sir Roger Moore appeared as a guest in the show?

977. What award did writer Eddie Braben win for his contribution to the show?

978. Which Australian singer, famed for hits including 'I Should Be So Lucky', appeared as a guest on the show?

979. What is the name of Mick Jagger's former wife who appeared as a celebrity guest in the show?

980. True or false: the show played for a time on Broadway in New York?

Pot Luck 3

Finally, why not see how many of the third set of 20 pot-luck questions, which all relate to Morecambe & Wise, you can answer correctly?

981. Who wrote the words to the song 'Bring Me Sunshine' – Sylvia Dee, Sylvia Hurst or Sylvia West?

982. Who first suggested that Eric and Ernie should perform together as a double act?

983. At what time did the studio audience recording of the 1977 Christmas show start – 7pm, 8pm or 9pm?

984. Which entertainer did Morecambe & Wise see making his cabaret debut at the Talk of the Town venue in May 1964 – Bruce Forsyth, Roy Hudd or Mike Yarwood?

985. True or false: Eric and Ernie appeared in a television advert for W.H.Smith?

986. On which breakfast television station did Ernie pay a moving tribute to Eric following his death?

987. Which legendary singer from Liverpool declared in a 1994 interview that *The Morecambe & Wise Show* was the most favourite of all the television shows he had ever appeared on?

988. True or false: actress Gemma Craven once played a sexy French maid in a memorable flat sketch on *The Morecambe & Wise Show*?

989. In which year did Eric and Ernie first record an album of songs and sketches?

990. Which year does Eric's son, Gary, recall as being the first time he can remember watching Morecambe & Wise on television – 1961, 1962 or 1963?

991. In a sketch on one of Morecambe & Wise's Thames shows that featured Eric as a bell ringer, how many bells did he use – five, six or seven?

992. True or false: Ernie was once described as 'The Jack Buchanan of tomorrow'?

993. Which *Yes Minister* actor appeared in a Sherlock Holmes sketch in a show Eric and Ernie made for Thames?

Did You Know?

The world may have been deprived of the magic of Morecambe & Wise if the one-time planned emigration of the Bartholomew family (Eric, his parents, uncle and aunty) had taken place.

994. During their short run at the Windmill Theatre in London, how many shows did Morecambe & Wise perform in a day – six, seven or eight?

995. What role did Eric play in a *Jungle Book* routine which was filmed for a Thames show?

996. True or false: in the much-loved 'Antony and Cleopatra' sketch, Eric held up a Roman standard that had the words 'Luton Town FC' written on it?

997. How many weeks did Eric and Ernie's 1964 pantomime run last – 16, 17 or 18?

998. True or false: actor Richard O'Sullivan appeared in *Morecambe & Wise's Christmas Special* in 1983?

999. True or false: Eric's son, Gary, used to work for Morecambe & Wise's one-time agent Billy Marsh?

1000. Which of Morecambe & Wise's films did Eric once discover being shown at a cinema in Portugal?

Eric Morecambe

1. John Eric Bartholomew.
2. 14 May 1926.
3. Molly Bunting.
4. George Formby.
5. 12.
6. Flanagan and Allen.
7. An audition with Jack Hylton.
8. True.
9. ENSA.
10. True.
11. Empire Theatre, Edinburgh.
12. 11 December 1952.
13. Margate.
14. 1953.
15. Austin Hereford.
16. 1956.
17. Gail.
18. Chips.
19. True.
20. 1968.
21. Walter Butterworth.
22. Portugal.
23. Charlie.
24. 1975.
25. Steven.

26. False, he couldn't swim.
27. Long John Silver.
28. Mike Fountain.
29. True.
30. EM 100.
31. Goaldiggers.
32. University of Lancashire.
33. 1979.
34. 1981.
35. *Late Flowering Love*.
36. *The Reluctant Vampire* and *The Vampire's Revenge*.
37. *The Passionate Pilgrim*.
38. *Eric Morecambe on Fishing*.
39. *World of Sport*.
40. *Funnyman*.
41. True.
42. Monday 28 May 1984.
43. Dickie Henderson.
44. *Stella*.
45. *Morecambe and Wife*.
46. £155.
47. *And Soul of*.
48. 2001.
49. £23,467.
50. A nursing home.

Ernie Wise

51. Ernest Wiseman.
52. Leeds.
53. 27 November 1925.
54. Harry and Connie Wiseman.
55. Carson and Kid.
56. Two guineas.
57. 1938.
58. True.
50. Arthur Askey.
60. Coalman's labourer.
61. Two.
62. Working as part of Lord John Sanger's Circus and Variety Tour.
63. Valentine's Day.
64. 18 January 1953.
65. Peterborough.
66. None.
67. True.
68. The assassination of President Kennedy.
69. 6½.
70. He swallowed a front tooth.
71. False.
72. *Gardeners' World*.
73. True.
74. *Looks Familiar*.
75. *Too Close for Comfort*.

76. 1 January 1985.
77. *What's My Line?*.
78. *Run for Your Wife*.
79. True.
80. *Aspel*.
81. *The Mystery of Edwin Drood*.
82. *Telly Addicts*.
83. True, the production was *The Mystery of Edwin Drood*.
84. Corda.
85. Eric Morecambe.
86. 1991.
87. *Wogan*.
88. Eddie Braben and Ernest Maxin.
89. *Sleeping Beauty*.
90. Three.
91. *Countdown*.
92. *Pebble Mill*.
93. River Thames.
94. Florida.
95. *Still On My Way to Hollywood*.
96. *The Importance of Being Ernie*.
97. 1995.
98. 21 March 1999.
99. Michael Grade.
100. Sid Green.

Pot Luck 1

101. 1950.
102. John Laurie, John Le Mesurier and Arthur Lowe.
103. 1976.
104. 43 years.
105. The Kaye Sisters.
106. Nick Munro.
107. Friday 11 February 1972.
108. Cliff Michelmore.
109. Room 405.
110. False, it was 1976.
111. 1973.
112. *Mr Mercury*.
113. Jimmy Durante.
114. Evil Eric.
115. 1960.
116. *Buster*.
117. Extremely Wealthy.
118. Tea.
119. The Queen Mother.
120. 1999.

Stage

121. Liverpool Empire.
122. One week.
123. Clapham Grand.
124. Personalities.

125. Green.
126. *This Is The Show*.
127. True.
128. False.
129. *and the Beanstalk*.
130. Hulme Hippodrome.
131. False.
132. *Riding Hood*.
133. Coventry.
134. *Dick Whittington*.
135. True.
136. 2s/3d.
137. Palace.
138. Page.
139. Ken Dodd.
140. Blackpool.
141. Winter Gardens.
142. Ardwick Hippodrome, Manchester.
143. *Let's Have Fun*.
144. False, it was six months.
145. Central Pier.
146. Weymouth.
147. Tommy Cooper.
148. Prince of Wales.
149. 1963.
150. *Show Time 1964*.

151. Bert Weedon.

152. False, it was Bill Roberton.

153. Palace Theatre.

154. £100,000.

155. False, he did, including Eric and Ernie's 1964 pantomime in Manchester.

156. Irving Berlin.

157. Sandy Powell.

158. 1967.

159. Leicester.

160. £105,640.

161. Great Yarmouth.

162. Winter Gardens, Bournemouth.

163. Bank raids.

164. True.

165. ABC, Exeter.

166. Five.

167. Sunblest.

168. True.

169. Guildhall.

170. False.

Radio

171. *You're Only Young Once* (often known as 'YOYO').

172. Deryck Guyler.

173. Manchester.

174. Peter Sellers.

175. False, it was 1953.

176. 26 March 1954.

177. *Playtime*.

178. Six.

179. 45.

180. True.

181. 1955.

182. *Seaside Nights*.

183. *What Did You Do In The War, Daddy?*

184. True.

185. *Hall of Fame*.

186. Percy Edwards.

187. 1977.

188. False.

189. 25 March 1978.

190. True.

Television

191. 1948.

192. *Party*.

193. *Running Wild*.

194. Three.

195. Ronnie Waldman.

196. 9.30pm.

197. True.

198. Amanda Barrie.

199. Bernard Bresslaw.

200. BBC Television Theatre, Shepherd's Bush, London.

201. 21 April 1954.

202. False, it was broadcast fortnightly.

203. 'Buried Morecambe & Wise in'.

204. Johnny Speight.

205. *Double Six*.

206. *Monkhouse*.

207. 12.

208. *Four Aces and a King*.

209. *Two of a Kind*.

210. False, it was broadcast from the Wood Green Empire, North London.

211. Nine.

212. 35.

213. True.

214. Thursday.

215. VAF (Variety Artists' Federation).

216. Number two.

217. 22.

218. 18 April 1964.

219. Bongo.

220. 'Moonlight Bay'.

221. False.

222. 76.

223. The Battle of Waterloo.

224. 10.
225. True.
226. BBC2.
227. *Pick Your Luck*.
228. Father Christmas.
229. True.
230. Conrad.
231. *Pencil and Paper*.
232. ITC Entertainment Group.
233. Series six.
234. Morey, Cambe and Wise.
235. Patricia Routledge.
236. 67.
237. Sausage, egg and chips.
238. Six.
239. *Piccadilly Palace*.
240. 31 March 1968.
241. Four times.
242. True.
243. False.
244. Bill Cotton Jr.
245. 69 editions.
246. Peter Cushing.
247. Nine.
248. 2 September 1968.
249. True.

250. 45 minutes.
251. Only part of one edition.
252. 1968.
253. Peter Knight.
254. 35.5%.
255. False, it was the 24 August 1969.
256. True.
257. Fenella Fielding.
258. True.
259. Percy Thrower.
260. Rain.
261. Hughie Green.
262. Vera Lynn.
263. Oggie.
264. Patrick Moore.
265. Francis Matthews.
266. Prince Charles.
267. True.
268. *Worked with*.
269. Richard Greene.
270. 'Monty On the Bonty'.
271. False, the comedian did make a brief appearance.
272. 65 minutes.
273. True.
274. A Fortnum and Mason's hamper.
275. Butler.

276. *Fools Rush In*.

277. False, Kenneth never appeared on the show.

278. Six.

279. Vanessa Redgrave.

280. Frank Williams.

281. Robin Hood.

282. Gene Kelly.

283. Robin Day.

284. 'Escape From Stalag 54'.

285. Mark Antony.

286. Frank Finlay.

287. Pete Murray.

288. Susan Hampshire.

289. Captain Knee Trembler.

290. True.

291. Adrian Fondle.

292. 12.

293. Gordon Jackson.

294. True.

295. 'Nobody Does it Like Me'.

296. 'Somethin' 'Bout You Baby I Like'.

297. He slowly climbed into a water trough where he lay down.

298. The tops both flew off.

299. He was pushed along the top of a bar and through part of a wall.

300. 'There's Nothing Like a Dame'.

301. Santa Claus.

302. Ada Bailey.

303. They blocked the duo from being seen by the viewers.

304. His wig.

305. False, it was Richard Greene.

306. He failed to catch it as it came back down.

307. A radio.

308. *Match of the Day*.

309. Negligee.

310. *In the Willows*.

311. False.

312. Eric Morecambe's Irresistible.

313. Four.

314. 20 minutes.

315. Anthony Sharp.

316. 'Exactly Like You'.

317. Felix Bowness.

318. Wormwood Scrubs.

319. Elephant John.

320. 7.45pm.

321. False.

322. Saturday 10 December 1977.

323. 28,835,000.

324. Michael Aspel, Richard Baker, Frank Bough, Philip Jenkinson, Barry Norman, Eddie Waring and Richard Whitmore.

325. Starkers and Crutch.

326. A Mini.

327. Sunday 11 December 1977.

328. 8.55pm.

329. True.

330. 1978.

331. ATV.

332. 33.

333. Sir Donald Sinden.

334. Dame Judi Dench.

335. Keith Beckett.

336. Teddington in Middlesex.

337. Leonard Sachs.

338. 1978.

339. Leonard Rossiter.

340. Anna.

341. Italia Conti Stage School.

342. Land Girls.

343. Anna Ford.

344. He couldn't open the piano lid.

345. He kept spinning it round on its perch.

346. True.

347. He blew it up.

348. Rolf Harris.

349. Peter Barkworth.

350. He kept stirring the water with a long dog biscuit.

351. Sylvester.

352. David Frost.

353. True.

354. Hugh Paddick.

355. 1980.

356. Terry Wogan.

357. Sir Alec Guinness.

358. A wig stand.

359. A ventriloquist's dummy.

360. Claudius, the King.

361. A chair.

362. 15.

363. 16.7 million.

364. Richard Briers.

365. Trevor Brooking.

366. Patricia Brake.

367. Henry Cooper.

368. James Hunt.

369. 'All That Jazz'.

370. An overcoat and cloth cap.

371. *Eric and Ernie's Variety Days*.

372. Patrick Mower.

373. Burt Kwouk.

374. Mark Stuart.

375. True.

376. False, only Ernie appeared on this show.

377. *Child's*.

378. Almost 12 million.

379. Liberty.

380. 14th.

381. 'The Stripper'.

382. Five.

383. Arsenal.

384. The 'Grieg piano concerto' sketch.

385. False.

386. A pipe.

387. True.

388. *Morecambe & Wise Encore*.

389. 'Evenin' all'.

390. True.

Eric and Ernie Live

391. Fairfield Halls, Croydon.

392. Johnny Wiltshire Orchestra.

393. False.

394. Sammy Davis Jr.

395. The bongos.

396. 'Slapping'.

397. 'Pretty Baby'.

398. False.

399. Two Old Men in Deckchairs.

400. 34 years.

401. 'Bring Me Sunshine'.

402. Graham Stephenson.

403. Alan More.

404. Delta Sound.

405. Thames Television.

406. 1987.

407. 60 minutes.

408. Polygram.

409. 66 minutes.

410. PG.

The Sweeney

411. Thames Television and Euston Films.

412. *Hearts and Minds*.

413. 23 November 1978.

414. John Thaw and Dennis Waterman.

415. John Thaw.

416. True.

417. Garfield Morgan.

418. Edward Hardwicke.

419. *This Week*.

420. Jean Boht.

421. True.

422. Donald Churchill and Ted Childs.

423. Lloyd Shirley and George Taylor.

424. NDV 656P.

425. Lakeside Club.

426. Columbo.

427. Jean.

428. Inside Eric's ventriloquist's doll.

429. Brayham's Fresh Fish.

430. Boxes of fish.

Supporting Cast

Ann Hamilton

431. Orsett, Essex.

432. 1959.

433. 1961.

434. *Little Me*.

435. Desdemona.

436. Maid Marian.

437. True.

438. False.

439. Ken Barlow.

440. 1987.

Janet Webb

441. Liverpool.

442. *A Funny Thing Happened on the Way to the Forum*.

443. *Way to Go*.

444. False.

445. Arthur Lowe.

446. True.

447. True.

448. *Whoops Baghdad!*

449. *Amorous.*

450. None.

Arthur Tolcher

451. 9 April 1922.

452. Bloxwich, Staffordshire.

453. 1939.

454. True.

455. 'Spanish Gypsy Dance'.

456. 1971.

457. True.

458. False.

459. BBC Radio 4.

460. 1987.

Special Guests

Dame Shirley Bassey

461. Cardiff, Wales.

462. 'He Needs Me'.

463. True.

464. Two.

465. 1971.

466. 'Smoke Gets in Your Eyes'.

467. One of her shoes got caught in part of the bottom step.

468. 1999.

469. 50.

470. False, it was 2007.

Peter Cushing

471. 26 May 1913.

472. Kenley, Surrey.

473. True.

474. Twice.

475. 1969.

476. King Arthur.

477. Hammer Films.

478. Paying him.

479. Grand Moff Tarkin.

480. 11 August 1994.

Hannah Gordon

481. Edinburgh, Scotland.

482. False.

483. *Port Wine*.

484. Two.

485. 'Windmills of Your Mind'.

486. 10 September 1980.

487. Ophelia.

488. *Change*.

489. Mrs Durrell.

490. *Joint Account.*

Dame Glenda Jackson

491. Birkenhead, Liverpool.

492. RADA.

493. 1971.

494. 3 June 1973.

495. 'Antony and Cleopatra'.

496. *A Touch of Class*.

497. She fell off the back of a large staircase.

498. 1978.

499. True.

500. 1992.

Penelope Keith

501. Sutton, Surrey.

502. True.

503. ATV Centre, Borehamwood.

504. Margot Ledbetter.

505. It was too short.

506. One.

507. *Stress*.

508. True.

509. *What's My Line*.

510. *To the Manor Born*.

Des O'Connor

511. Stepney, East End, London.

512. 1953.

513. True.

514. 'Those six or seven people probably made all the difference'.

515. 1972.

516. True.

517. Desperate.

518. False.

519. True.

520. *Countdown*.

André Previn

521. 1971.

522. In the back of a taxi.

523. Chicago.

524. Preview and Privet.

525. Jump up into the air.

526. There was some laughter from the audience.

527. True.

528. 1982.

529. Wolfgang Amadeus Mozart.

530. *No Minor Chords*.

Sir Cliff Richard

531. Lucknow, India.

532. 1958.

533. The Shadows.

534. 1961.

535. A model aircraft.

536. A banana.
537. 'Living Doll'.
538. A mop.
539. 1986.
540. 1995.

Dame Diana Rigg

541. Doncaster, South Yorkshire.
542. *The Avengers*.
543. *On Her Majesty's Secret Service*.
544. Nell Gwynn.
545. Broughton Castle, Banbury, Oxon.
546. 17 November 1975.
547. 'That's all folks!'
548. True.
549. *Follies*.
550. True.

Angela Rippon

551. 1975.
552. 1976.
553. True.
554. *Eurovision Song Contest*.
555. False.
556. The wedding of Prince Charles and Lady Diana Spencer.
557. *Come Dancing*.
558. True.

559. 2004.

560. *Anything Goes*.

Complete The Names

Special Guests

561. Redgrave.

562. Magnusson.

563. Olivier.

564. Carmichael.

565. Sooty.

566. Whitfield.

567. Kate.

568. David.

569. Peter.

570. Ian.

571. Richardson.

572. Lenska.

573. Robert.

574. Jimmy.

575. Peter.

576. Dors.

577. Eve.

578. Kennedy.

579. Yehudi.

580. Sleep.

Singers and Musical Acts

581. Bruvvers.

582. Sammes.

583. King.

584. Parnell.

585. Four.

586. Kaye.

587. Lyttelton.

588. Clark.

589. New.

590. Dreamers.

591. Cotton.

592. Hermits.

593. Munro.

594. Jones.

595. Four.

596. Hill.

597. Distel.

598. Mouskouri.

599. Dee.

600. Vaughan.

Production Team

Johnny Ammonds

601. Radio sound-effects operative.

602. *In Town*.

603. Worth.
604. Val Doonican.
605. 1975.
606. *Horse Feathers*.
607. False.
608. Three.
609. True.
610. *Set*.

Eddie Braben

611. Liverpool.
612. 1956.
613. Charlie Chester.
614. True.
615. Liverpool Empire.
616. Lena Horne.
617. 1972.
618. 14.
619. The Golden Triangle.
620. They both collected clocks.

Bill Cotton

621. 1928.
622. *The Billy Cotton Bandshow*.
623. True.
624. 1967.
625. Like a divorce.

626. 1978.
627. 1998.
628. 1995.
629. 2001.
630. 2006.

Mike Craig

631. Batley, Yorkshire.
632. Dewsbury Empire.
633. 1964.
634. 1,200.
635. Light entertainment producer.
636. True.
637. Four.
638. True.
639. *The Day War Broke Out*.
640. *Wireless*.

Barry Cryer

641. Leeds, Yorkshire.
642. True.
643. 1969.
644. *I'm Sorry I Haven't a Clue*.
645. *Joker's Wild*.
646. True.
647. True.
648. Kenny Everett.

649. Sid Colin.

650. 2001.

Lord Lew Grade

651. True.

652. 1906.

653. 1926.

654. ITC.

655. True.

656. False, it was 1969.

657. Leslie Grade and Bernard Delfont.

658. 1976.

659. The Muppets.

660. *Lew Grade, Still Dancing: My Story*.

Sid Green and Dick Hills

661. 1928.

662. 17 January 1926.

663. 1961.

664. True.

665. *Those Two Fellers*.

666. True.

667. Frankie Howerd.

668. 1983.

669. 1999.

670. 6 June 1996.

Philip Jones
671. 1927.
672. Radio Luxembourg.
673. 1955.
674. *Thank Your Lucky Stars*.
675. 1961.
676. 1977.
677. True.
678. 1983.
679. True.
680. 2004.

John Junkin
681. 29 January 1930.
682. True.
683. Tony Hancock.
684. True.
685. *Junkin*.
686. Alf Garnett's milkman.
687. *Cheeky*.
688. Ernie Johnson.
689. *The Impressionable John Culshaw*.
690. 2006.

Ernest Maxin
691. Upton Park.
692. *Norman*.

693. False, he produced just one.

694. Dave Allen.

695. Torquay.

696. 1970.

697. True.

698. 13.

699. 1977.

700. False.

Pot Luck 2

701. Roy Castle.

702. False.

703. Monte Cristo.

704. Six.

705. True.

706. 1979.

707. Penny Morrell.

708. Ernie's wife.

709. False.

710. 1970.

711. His first grandchild, Amelia Faye Jarvis.

712. True.

713. Liberace.

714. 1953.

715. Comic Heritage (now The Heritage Foundation).

716. False.

717. Harpenden Public Hall.

718. True.

719. 'The Naked Village'.

720. True.

Film

The Intelligence Men

721. True.

722. Ernie Sage.

723. *The Intelligence Men or M.I.5. Plus 2 Equals 0*.

724. The Rank Organisation.

725. Pinewood Studios.

726. 1965.

727. False, the running time is 104 mins.

728. Manchester.

729. *Spylarks*.

730. Robert Asher.

731. Jack Asher.

732. Philip Green.

733. Eleanor Fazan.

734. Peter Blackmore.

735. The Houses of Parliament.

736. Major Cavendish.

737. Paris.

738. Bob Todd.

739. Colonel Grant.

740. Terence Alexander.

741. True.

742. A desk.

743. Madame Petrovna.

744. False.

745. Johnny Briggs.

746. Warren Mitchell.

747. Cosmopolitan.

748. True.

749. The Rest.

750. He crashed.

751. The Roxy.

752. 7.30pm.

753. Row E seat 4.

754. A cinema usherette.

755. He got caught in between a courting couple.

756. He was stabbed.

757. *Swan Lake*.

758. Opera House, Covent Garden.

759. Written on her dressing table mirror.

760. They ended up dancing on stage.

That Riviera Touch

761. Eric Simpson.

762. Ernie Clarke.

763. Paul Stassino.

764. Cliff Owen.

765. Hugh Stewart.

766. Ron Goodwin.

767. 1966.

768. Traffic wardens.

769. Buckingham Palace.

770. A sign on a lorry.

771. British United Airlines.

772. Aeroport De Touquet.

773. False, it was the third.

774. They went to the bar.

775. His left.

776. On his boat.

777. Over the garage at the villa.

778. True.

779. Villa Tulipe.

780. Because it was free.

781. Into the sea through a trap door in the kitchen floor.

782. He kept getting knocked in the face with the ball.

783. In a special attachment to the fuel pipe.

784. Wear it.

785. 25, 9 and 0.

786. Hotel Splendid.

787. 220 francs.

788. Frogs' legs.

789. He fell over the edge and down on to a dinner table below, where a group of people were eating dinner.

790. In a money belt.

791. A new car.

792. She took her bikini top off.

793. He fell over and lost his glasses.

794. Bits of newspaper.

795. By using firework rockets.

796. Riviera Sub-Aqua Club.

797. Turn on the windscreen wipers.

798. He was shot.

799. He crashed in into the sea.

800. No one is quite sure!

The Magnificent Two

801. Toy soldiers.

802. 1967.

803. 5th.

804. 100 minutes.

805. Michael Pertwee.

806. Eric Rattray.

807. Ernest Steward.

808. *What Happened at Campo Grande*.

808. Carla.

810. Cecil Parker.

811. David Charlesworth.

812. True.

813. A drunken soldier.

814. Isobel Black.

815. False, he was played by Martin Benson.

816. Paco.

817. Tyler Butterworth.

818. *You Only Live Twice*.

819. Black Park.

820. Sean Connery.

821. True.

822. An angry dog.

823. He fell out of a railway carriage.

824. Have a siesta.

825. In a barrel.

826. One million pesos.

827. One.

828. Men and women shared.

829. In his tea leaves.

830. Four.

831. A great liberator.

832. He made up his own speech.

833. A hearse.

834. A military museum.

835. Wax dummies.

836. He shackled them to a museum piece called the giant crusher.

837. Cheating.

838. By stripping to just their bikini tops and bottoms.

839. Remain living with the female revolutionaries.

840. False.

Night Train to Murder

841. Joe McGrath.

842. Eric Morecambe, Ernie Wise and Joe McGrath.

843. Rod McLaren and Jack Hobbs.

844. Philip Jones.

845. True.

846. 3 January 1985.

847. Shirley Teece.

848. Fulton Mackay.

849. Lysette Anthony.

850. Pamela Salem.

851. True.

852. Uncle Felix.

853. False.

854. 1946.

855. Comedy double act.

856. Ben Aris.

857. Roger Brierly.

858. Edward Judd.

859. Dame Flora.

860. At a funeral.

861. Carlisle.

862. Monday 23 September.

863. 6.30pm and 8.45pm.

864. *Fools Rush In*.

865. Her Majesty's Theatre.

866. Des O'Connor.

867. False, it was Ernie who wore it.

868. Austin Hall.

869. GBH 287.

870. False, it was snowing.

871. Cards.

872. 'We'll Gather Lilacs'.

873. True.

874. *Passport to Death*.

875. *Tit-Bits*.

876. A stone slab fell through the top.

877. Whitehall 1-2 1-2.

878. True.

879. 'Little Sir Echo'.

880. 2003.

Records

881. 'Later'.

882. 'Shadow'.

883. 'Blues'.

884. 'Chickens'.

885. 'Keats'.

886. 'Ernie'.

887. Khasiland'.

888. 'Body'.

889. 'Window'.

890. 'Ern'.

891. 'Corner'.

892. 'Pilbroch'.

893. 'The Guys'.

894. 'Youth'.

895. 'You're Here'.

896. "B".

897. 'Let You Go'.

898. 'Don't You Agree?'

899. 'Jells'.

900. 'Happiest Christmas'.

Catchphrases

901. 'Join'.

902. 'Fool'.

903. 'Honest'.

904. 'Novelty'.

905. 'Of that'.

906. 'Think of it so far?'

907. 'When I am talking to you'.

908. 'Much further'.

909. 'Half a star'.

910. 'Off'.

Books

911. *Cricklewood*.

912. Kevin Keegan.

913. *Good Morning Boys – Will Hay*.

914. *A Celebration*.

915. *Roy of The Rovers*.

916. 1975.

917. *There's No Answer to That! – The Autobiography of Morecambe & Wise*.

918. *The Morecambe & Wise Joke Book*.

919. Dennis Holman.

920. *Harpenden*.

921. *Eric Morecambe: Unseen*.

922. *Eric, Ernie And Me*.

923. Robert Lindsay.

924. Bruce Crowther and Mike Pinfold.

925. True.

926. 1986.

927. 1972.

928. *Harvest*.

929. False.

930. 261.

Luton Town FC

931. 1885.

932. 1897.

933. One.

934. 31 January 1970.
935. 7 November 1975.
936. True.
937. Negatives.
938. The Eric Morecambe Suite.
939. A hole in Peter's costume tights.
940. 'There is only one Eric Morecambe'.

Bring Me Sunshine Tribute Show

941. London Palladium.
942. Thames Television.
943. 9 November 1984.
944. 28 December 1984.
945. 150 minutes.
946. British Heart Foundation.
947. Prince Philip.
948. Ernie Wise.
949. Benny Hill.
950. False, it was Irving Davies.
951. Billy Marsh.
952. Mark Stuart.
953. Philip Jones and Louis Benjamin.
954. 72.
955. Cannon and Ball.
956. Jim Davidson.
957. True.
958. Leslie Crowther.

959. Nanette Newman.
960. True.

The Eric Morecambe Statue

961. Morecambe.
962. Graham Ibbeson.
963. Six years.
964. The Queen.
965. 23 July 1999.
966. 103.
967. False.
968. 'Bring Me Sunshine'.
969. A pair of binoculars.
970. True.

The Play What I Wrote

971. Sean Foley and Hamish McColl.
972. 27 September 2001.
973. Everyman Playhouse, Liverpool.
974. Kenneth Branagh.
975. Michael Starke.
976. True.
977. The Laurence Olivier Award.
978. Kylie Minogue.
979. Jerry Hall.
980. True.

Pot Luck 3

981. Sylvia Dee.

982. Eric's mother, Sadie Bartholomew.

983. 8pm.

984. Bruce Forsyth.

985. True.

986. *TV-am*.

987. Paul McCartney.

988. True.

989. 1964.

990. 1961.

991. Seven.

992. True.

993. Nigel Hawthorne.

994. Six.

995. Baloo the Bear.

996. True.

997. 16.

998. False.

999. True.

1000. *The Magnificent Two*.

Eric Morecambe and Ernie Wise: A Chronology

1925

Ernie Wise (full real name: Ernest Wiseman) is born in Leeds, Yorkshire, on 27 November 1925 to parents Harry and Connie Wiseman.

1926

Eric Morecambe (full real name: John Eric Bartholomew) is born in Morecambe, Lancashire, on 14 May to parents George and Sadie Bartholomew.

1932

Ernie starts his show business life by joining his father, Harry, in a double act. They name themselves 'Carson and Kid' and perform in working men's clubs at weekends in order to help with the family finances.

1936

Eric begins dancing classes at Miss Hunter's dancing school in Morecambe and performs in a song and dance act with a girl from the area called Molly Bunting.

1938

At the tender age of 12, Eric leaves school to start a full-time career in show business. As a child performer he impersonates (on his own) both of the much-loved double act, Flanagan and Allen. The impresario Bryan Michie auditions Ernie at the Leeds Empire.

1939

Eric wins a talent competition staged by *Melody Maker*. His prize was to audition for the impresario Jack Hylton. At his audition, Eric meets a certain Ernest Wiseman for the first time. Ernie appears in the famous *Band Wagon* show with the legendary comedian, Arthur Askey.

1941

Eric and Ernie perform as a double act together for the very first time at the Liverpool Empire. During this year, Adelaide Hall's husband, Bert Hicks, suggests that Eric change his second name to the place where he was born. Thus the performer now becomes forever known as Eric Morecambe.

1943

Eric and Ernie – now known as Morecambe & Wise – take their place before a BBC microphone and perform on the radio shows *Strike a New Note* and *Youth Must Have its Fling*. Ernie receives his call-up paper and will spend the following two years in the merchant navy.

1944

Eric is called up and spends time down in the mines as a Bevin Boy in Accrington.

1945

Poor health results in Eric being invalided out and thus excused from his role as a Bevin Boy.

1946

Morecambe & Wise – the act that will in time become the highlight of Christmas viewing for millions of people in the UK – re-form.

1947

Morecambe & Wise appear in Lord John Sanger's Circus and Variety Tour. Ernie meets his future wife, Doreen Blythe.

1948

Morecambe & Wise appear for the first time on BBC television.

1950

The double act sign with Frank Pope, and he becomes their agent. Things become brighter as the act start to play dates at theatres on the Moss Empire's circuit.

1952

Eric meets his future wife, Joan Bartlett, at the Empire Theatre, Edinburgh. The couple later marry on 11 December of the same year. Ernie proposes to his future wife, Doreen, on Valentine's Day in the same year.

1953

Eric's daughter, Gail, is born, Morecambe & Wise finally achieve their own radio series, *You're Only Young Once,* and Ernie and Doreen marry on 18 January. The year also sees Eric pass his driving test.

1954

The year which first saw Eric and Ernie take to the small screen with their own television series *Running Wild*. Sadly, it is not declared a success by the critics of the day.

1956

Eric's son, Gary, is born. Eric and Joan also purchase their first house. Their new home is located in Finchley, north London.

Television bosses once again come knocking on Morecambe & Wise's door. This time it was the turn of ITV and the act appear on *The Winfred Atwell Show*. Eric and Ernie's spots are written by the future *Till Death Us Do Part* writer, Johnny Speight.

1958
Eric and Ernie tour Australia for six months.

1960
Billy Marsh replaces Frank Pope as Morecambe & Wise's agent.

1961
Lew Grade (later made Lord Lew Grade) agrees to give 'The Boys' their own television series at ATV. At last, *The Morecambe & Wise Show* (subtitle: *Two of a Kind*) can be seen by viewers on the small screen. Morecambe & Wise also appear on their very first *Royal Variety Show*. Finally, Eric, Joan and their two children, Gail and Gary, move to their first Harpenden home.

1963
Eric and Ernie are presented with their first BAFTA award. During the award ceremony the tragic news filters through the audience, while the double act are both on stage receiving their award, that President Kennedy has been assassinated.

1964
Eric calls Ringo Starr 'Bongo' during The Beatles' memorable, but sadly only, appearance on *The Morecambe & Wise Show*. The summer season sees Morecambe & Wise appear in *Show Time 1964* at the Wellington Pier Pavilion, Great Yarmouth. Ed Sullivan jets Eric and Ern to New York for their first appearance

on *The Ed Sullivan Show*. The double act also travel to Pinewood Studios in Buckinghamshire to make the first of three feature films for the Rank Organisation, *The Intelligence Men*. To round off the year, the tall one with the glasses and the short one with the fat hairy legs appear in pantomime at the Palace Theatre, Manchester, in *The Sleeping Beauty*. The pantomime has a box office advance of £100,000. The year also sees Eric and Ernie honoured by the Variety Club.

1965

It's back to Pinewood Studios for Morecambe & Wise to make, arguably, the best of their three Rank Organisation-made films, *That Riviera Touch*. Location work sees the duo (and their wives) travel to the south of France.

1966

Eric and Ernie see out their three-film contract with Rank by making *The Magnificent Two*. Sadly, Ernie's father, Harry Wiseman, passes away on 18 February of this year.

1967

Morecambe & Wise appear at the ABC Theatre, Great Yarmouth (since demolished) in a record-breaking summer season.

1968

TV's loss is the BBC's gain as Morecambe & Wise are both signed to the corporation by Bill Cotton Jr. However, after just one series, Eric suffers his first heart attack. A man called Walter Butterworth helps Eric to a hospital in Leeds.

1969

With Eric having recovered from his first heart attack, Morecambe & Wise start work again at the BBC. Dipping their toe back in the water, the double act present a special compilation series before commencing work on a new series. Former Ken Dodd gag-writer, Eddie Braben, becomes Eric and Ernie's principal television series scriptwriter. Eric and Ernie both win a BAFTA award.

1970

Eric is voted pipe-smoker of the year as well as becoming a director of Luton Town FC. Morecambe & Wise win yet another BAFTA award.

1971

The year sees Morecambe & Wise welcoming both André Previn and Glenda Jackson on to their show. Eric and Ernie win another BAFTA award and are honoured by the Radio Industries Organisation.

1972

Morecambe & Wise add yet another BAFTA award to their collection. The double act also attends the unveiling of their wax effigies at Madame Tussauds in London, on Friday 11 February 1972.

1973

Dennis Holman 'referees' on the double acts' book *Eric and Ernie – The Autobiography of Morecambe & Wise*. Eric is profiled by Kenneth Tynan in the *Observer* magazine. This year sees the duo with another BAFTA to add to their collection.

1974

Eric and Joan adopt a son, Steven. Morecambe & Wise are honoured by both the Variety Club and Water Rats.

1975

Eric gives a memorable speech after giving his daughter, Gail, away at her wedding. Morecambe & Wise's 'bank raid' appearances this year include five Sunday concerts at the Britannia Pier Theatre, Great Yarmouth.

1976

Morecambe & Wise are both honoured with the OBE, the freedom of the City of London and by the Variety Club. Eric is presented with an honorary degree by the University of Lancashire. Unhappily, the year sees the untimely death of Eric's father, George Bartholomew.

1977

Eric's mother, Sadie Bartholomew, passes away. Morecambe & Wise's last-ever Christmas show for the BBC, and last show before they leave the corporation for Thames, is seen by 28,835,000 viewers.

1978

Morecambe & Wise leave the BBC and sign to Thames Television. From now on, all of Morecambe & Wise's shows will be made at Thames's headquarters in Teddington, Middlesex. Eric and Ernie's first Christmas special for the broadcaster features former Prime Minister, Harold Wilson. The Variety Club honour Morecambe & Wise with another award.

1979

Eric suffers his second heart attack and then undergoes heart bypass surgery. As well as a Christmas special for Thames, Eric also appears in a short film for the East Anglian-based ITV franchise-holder, Anglia Television, which is based on the works of writer John Betjeman.

1980

Step forward Eric the novelist, as he devotes part of the year to writing *Mr Lonely*, while still recovering from heart surgery. Eric appears in a second film for Anglia Television, while also appearing in a first series and another Christmas special with Ernie for Thames.

1981

Eric's first novel, *Mr Lonely*, is published and receives praise by the critics. Morecambe & Wise see themselves inducted into the TV Hall of Fame as well as recording another series for Thames Television.

1982

Eric writes the first of two children's novels, *The Reluctant Vampire*, as well as taking part in another series for ITV London franchise-holder, Thames Television. Eric also films scenes for the silent film *The Passionate Pilgrim*.

1983

Eric films further scenes for the silent film *The Passionate Pilgrim*, writes the second of his two novels for children, *The Vampire's Revenge*, records another series for Thames with Ernie, undertakes a film project for Thames Television/Euston Films, *Night Train to Murder*, and does Morecambe & Wise's last-ever Christmas special.

1984

Editing is completed on Morecambe & Wise's film project, *Night Train to Murder*, while Eric writes the book *Eric Morecambe on Fishing*, which includes a special foreword by his comedy partner Ernie. The nation goes into mourning after Eric dies after suffering a third heart attack following a spellbinding performance at The Roses Theatre, Tewkesbury, on 28 May. Eric had been interviewed on stage by long-time friend and fellow performer, Stan Stennett, whom Morecambe & Wise had worked with during their careers. Ernie Wise pays a moving tribute to his late performer on *TV-am* and by reading out the words to 'Bring Me Sunshine' at his comedy partner's funeral. The end of the year sees Thames Television broadcast a tribute to Eric Morecambe staged at the London Palladium, which is hosted by Ernie Wise and includes a large cast of well-known performers. The show raises much-needed funds for the British Heart Foundation.

1985

Ernie makes the first-ever mobile phone call in Britain on New Year's Day. Ernie later tours Australia with his one-man show, which includes clips shown on a screen of his television work with Eric. However, sadness somewhat overshadows this venture for Ernie with the death of his mother, Connie Wiseman, at the age of 85, 19 years after her husband's death. Eric's son, Gary, completes an unfinished adult novel written by his father entitled *Stella*. The book is then published. Eric's widow, Joan, also has her book, *Morecambe and Wife*, published.

1987

Gary Morecambe's book, *The Illustrated Morecambe*, is published. Ernie plays the role of William Cartwright in the West End musical *The Mystery of Edwin Drood*. Scottish actress and singer, Lulu, also appears in the cast. Following the closure of the musical, Ernie is back on stage only a few months later this year in the hit Ray Cooney farce *Run for Your Wife*, taking over the role of Detective Sargeant Porterhouse, recently vacated by Eric Sykes.

1989

Ernie helps to raise funds for the heart charity Corda by flying round the world in 80 hours dressed as Phileas Fogg. Ernie takes Marty Christian of the New Seekers as his manservant.

1990

Ernie has his autobiography, *Still On My Way to Hollywood*, published and dedicates it to his late comedy partner, Eric.

1991

Ernie is the subject of the long-running tribute programme *This is Your Life*. Ernie finds himself presented with the 'Big Red Book' by Michael Aspel, who 14 years previously had appeared in the 'South Pacific' routine with Ernie and his comedy partner and a host of newsreaders. Ernie also briefly appears on the chat show, *Wogan*, which is the last-ever programme to be broadcast from the BBC Television Theatre by the corporation prior to its sale.

1992

Ernie pays a moving tribute on radio to Benny Hill, who passes away during the Easter weekend. Ernie ends this year by playing the King in the pantomime, *Sleeping Beauty*, in Windsor, Berkshire, with Bryan Burdon.

1993

Ernie is the subject of a BBC documentary entitled *The Importance of Being Ernie*.

1994

Ten years following Eric's untimely death, the biography *Morecambe & Wise: Behind the Sunshine*, by Gary Morecambe and Martin Stirling, is published and proves to be a best-seller. The BBC marks the 10th anniversary of Eric's death by showing a high-rating series of compilation programmes which are hosted by prolific writer and stand-up comedian, Ben Elton.

1995

Ernie Wise announces his retirement from show business at the age of 70 and Comic Heritage unveils a special plaque, which honours Eric, in London.

1996

A viewers' poll (marking the 60th anniversary of the BBC, Morecambe & Wise's one-time employers) reveals that Morecambe & Wise are their favourite performers of all time.

1998

Christmas sees a special edition of a BBC *Omnibus* programme entitled *The Heart and Soul of Eric Morecambe*. Readers of the *Radio Times* vote the duo the 'Best TV Comedy Stars of All Time', and Graham McCann's biography of the double act, *Morecambe & Wise*, is published.

1999

The untimely death is announced on 21 March of Ernie at the age of 73. Michael Grade reads the eulogy at Ernie's funeral. Morecambe & Wise receive a posthumous BAFTA fellowship. On a happier note, Graham Ibbeson's statue of Eric Morecambe is unveiled on the seafront at Morecambe in Lancashire by the Queen. The ceremony takes place on 23 January of this year and the unveiling of the statue is accompanied by the playing of the song 'Bring Me Sunshine'. The statue of Eric is surrounded by 103 celebrity names, all of whom appeared with the duo on television. The year, however, also sees the sad death of one-time co-writer of *The Morecambe & Wise Show*, Sid Green, who dies only days before Ernie.

2000

The first year of the millennium sees the announcement that an internet poll has voted Eric the greatest British comedian of the 20th century.

2001

ITV first broadcasts the television documentary on Eric entitled *The Unforgettable Eric Morecambe*. The tribute stage show *The Play What I Wrote* debuts on 27 September at the Everyman Playhouse, Liverpool. The show is directed by the well-known actor and film director Kenneth Branagh. The show later travels to the West End of London, and takes up residence at Wyndham's Theatre for a special run.

2002

It is revealed that Eric has been placed at 32nd place in a list of all-time Great Britons. The tribute show *The Play What I Wrote* goes from strength to strength and wins two Olivier Awards.

2003

The Play What I Wrote crosses the Atlantic and plays with critical success on Broadway in New York. The production finds itself shortlisted for a Tony Award.

2006

Eric's brown Rolls-Royce, registration EM 100, is sold at auction for £23,467.

2008

The year starts off with the broadcast on BBC1 of arguably the best Morecambe & Wise-related documentary to date: *Morecambe & Wise: In Their Own Words*. The documentary is presented by self-confessed Eric and Ernie fan, Jonathan Ross. One of Eric's pipes sells for £155.00 on the website eBay during the January of this year.

Although sadly Eric Morecambe OBE and Ernie Wise OBE are no longer with us, their legacy lives on. So this is by no means the end of the story. But I will leave it to Paul Zenon to eloquently sum up the magic of Morecambe & Wise in his Afterword.

Afterword

Paul Zenon is Britain's top trickster with several hundred television appearances and over 20 years' experience performing in every type of venue in around 30 countries.

'If you read one of their scripts never having seen Morecambe & Wise, it might well strike you as not being particularly funny. It's the bits that aren't said that make it – Eric's (apparent) deviation from script and his priceless reactions, body language, double-takes and pauses. His face seems to paint a vivid picture of his thought processes as they happen and builds huge anticipation for the next line; it's like the whirring of cogs before the clock chimes or an anticipatory drum roll before the cymbal crash – and you know it's going to be a big one by the expression of serene, amused confidence on Ernie's face that could only come from decades treading the boards in tandem.

Much comedy these days has a fairly narrow demographic; different niches for different social groups. For younger people it tends to be intellectually clever; politically or socially astute; or generally confrontational or cruel in some way – there's usually a target. It's difficult to imagine a group of teenagers or younger kids these days being held spellbound as we were by a couple of middle-aged blokes just being plain daft; they had no agenda other than laughter. What Eric and Ernie did have above all else was warmth; behind Eric's bluster and mischief and Ernie's pomposity and pretension there was never a hint of real animosity towards anyone – not even Des O'Connor!'

Paul Zenon

Websites

This page contains a list of recommended websites that relate to Morecambe & Wise.

Gail Morecambe – Morecambe Moments

Morecambe Moments was founded in 2001 by Gail Morecambe, watercolour artist and daughter of Eric Morecambe:
www.morecambemoments.com

Eric and Ern – the Morecambe & Wise Tribute Website

www.ericandern.co.uk

The Morecambe & Wise Homepage

www.morecambeandwise.co.uk

A Tribute to Morecambe & Wise

http://ericandernie.homestead.com

Bibliography

To aid with my research I watched a great deal of Morecambe & Wise's work on DVD and video. I also watched a seemingly endless collection of documentaries that relate to Eric Morecambe and/or Ernie Wise. Most important in my quest for Morecambe & Wise-related facts and figures have been several books written on Eric and/or Morecambe & Wise. The excellent books that I have used for reference are:

Eddie Braben *The Best of Morecambe & Wise – A Celebration* (Virgin Publishing, 1999).

Eddie Braben *Morecambe & Wise: their funniest jokes, one-liners and sketches* (Ebury Press, 2003).

Eddie Braben *The Book What I Wrote – Eric, Ernie And Me* (Hodder and Stoughton, 2004).

Roy Castle *Roy Castle – Now and Then* (Robson Books, 1994).

William Cook (editor) *Eric Morecambe Unseen* (HarperCollins, 2005).

Jane Harboard and Jeff Wright *40 Years of British Television* (Index, 1994).

Mark Lewisohn *Radio Times Guide to Comedy* (BBC Worldwide, Limited, 1998).

Graham McCann *Morecambe & Wise* (Fourth Estate, 1999).

Eric Morecambe *Mr Lonely* (Eyre Methuen, 1981).

Eric Morecambe and Ernie Wise *The Morecambe & Wise Special* (Weidenfeld & Nicolson, 1977).

BIBLIOGRAPHY

Eric Morecambe, Ernie Wise and Dennis Holman *Eric and Ernie – The Autobiography of Morecambe & Wise* (A Star Book published by W.H. Allen, 1974).

Gary Morecambe *Eric Morecambe – Life's Not Hollywood, it's Cricklewood* (BBC Books, 2003).

Gary Morecambe and Martin Sterling *Memories of Eric* (André Deutsch, 1999).

Gary Morecambe and Martin Sterling *Morecambe & Wise – Behind the Sunshine* (Robson Books, 2001).

Jeremy Norvick *Morecambe & Wise You Can't See the Join* (Chameleon Books, 1997).

Michael Sellers and Gary Morecambe *Hard Act to Follow – Intimate Stories of Life with Superstar Parents* (Blake Publishing, 1997).

Ernie Wise with Trevor Barnes *Still On My Way to Hollywood* (Gerald Duckworth, 1990).